American Language Hub

STARTER B
Workbook

with Key + access to Audio

macmillan education

Macmillan Education
4 Crinan Street
London N1 9XW
A division of Macmillan Education Limited

Companies and representatives throughout the world

American Language Hub Starter B Workbook with Key
ISBN 978-1-380-04681-9
American Language Hub Starter B Workbook with Key + access to
Audio ISBN 978-1-380-04675-8

Written by Signature Manuscripts

Signature Manuscripts has asserted their right to be identified as the author of this work in accordance with the Copyright, Designs and Patents Act 1988.

First published 2020

Original design by emc design ltd
Page make-up by SPi Global
Illustrated by Nigel Dobbyn (Beehive Illustration) pp39, 48, 50, 51
Cover design based on original design by Restless
Cover photograph by Getty Images/Valentinrussanov
Picture research by Emily Taylor

The author and publishers would like to thank the following for permission to reproduce their photographs:
Alamy p52(l), Alamy/Hero Images Inc p45, Alamy/IanDagnall Computing p57(br), Alamy/Leithan Partnership t/a The Picture Pantry p57(cmr); **EyeEm** p64; **Getty Images** p40(mr), Getty Images/Andresr p70, Getty Images/Thomas Barwick p44(tl), Getty Images/Bettmann Archive p52(r), Getty Images/Blend Images p73, Getty Images/Caiaimage/Robert Daly p55, Getty Images/Caiaimage/Tom Merton p67, Getty Images/Counter p74(tl), Getty Images/Richard Cummins p62(tr), Getty Images/Nick David p39, Getty Images/DGLimages pp44(cl), 46, Getty Images/Dorling Kindersley p57(cml), Getty Images/Erik Dreyer p56(r), Getty Images/Charles Eshelman p56(l), Getty Images/EyeEm/Pablo Benitez Lope p65, Getty Images/EyeEm/Rhoda Rochelle Ocon p63(r), Getty Images/EyeEm/Chaloemphon Wanitcharoentham p62(mr), Getty Images/Grki p59, Getty Images/Steven Han p50, Getty Images/Hero Images p47, Getty Images/Andrew Holt p62(tl), Getty Images/Istvan Kadar Photography p53, Getty Images/iStockphoto pp48, 57(cl), Getty Images/Johnnyknez p72, Getty Images/Hannah Mentz p61(r), Getty Images/Chris Mouyiaris p62(br), Getty Images/Naufal MQ p71, Getty Images/Michael Pasdzior p57(tr), Getty Images/John Phillips/The LIFE Picture Collection p54, Getty Images/Recep-bg p61(l), Getty Images/RnDmS p62(bl), Getty Images/Robas p68(tl), Getty Images/Tim Robberts p68(bl), Getty Images/SHansche p75, Getty Images/SKA p44(br), Getty Images/SolStock p40(tr), Getty Images/South_agency p74(bl), Getty Images/Skynesher p40(br), Getty Images/Valentinrussanov p42, Getty Images/Klaus Vedfelt p43, Getty Images/Westend61 pp60, 66, 69, Getty Images/ZargonDesign p41; **PeopleImages** p63(tl); **PhotoDisc**/Getty Images p58.

Printed and bound in Mexico
by Compañía Editorial Ultra, S.A. de C.V.

2021 2020
04 03 02 01

Contents

GRAMMAR
can/can't

A Complete the text with *can* or *can't* and the correct form of the verbs in parentheses.

WE NEED YOUR HELP!

Summer camp

1 ___ (*you / dive*), climb or swim? We need your help on our amazing summer camp. We 2 ___ (*teach*) sports like basketball and soccer, but we 3 ___ (*not do*) everything! With your special abilities, you 4 ___ (*help*) us teach young people important sports skills. We want people who 5 ___ (*do*) different things.

6 ___ (*you / help*)? Are you free for one week in the summer? We pay you and give you food and a room. It's not a problem if you 7 ___ (*not drive*) – there's a bus every day.

For more information, please contact
sportscampsummer@campservices.net.

B Complete the sentences with the phrases in the box.

can fly	can hold	Can you	can you do
can't cook	can't speak	I can't	we can

1 I ___ my breath for nearly a minute underwater.
2 **A:** Can you dive?
B: No, ___.
3 I ___ French, but I can speak German and Spanish.
4 ___ climb without a rope?
5 He only eats in restaurants because he ___.
6 What activities ___ in your town?
7 Some birds ___ 10,000 kilometers.
8 **A:** Can both of you swim?
B: Yes, ___.

C Use the prompts to make sentences.

1 He / play the piano / not the guitar.
He can play the piano but he can't play the guitar.
2 She / climb a tree / not a wall.
___
3 He / swim in a pool / not in the ocean.
___
4 They / play soccer / not basketball.
___
5 You / drive a car / not a bus.
___
6 She / make an omelette / not make a cake.
___
7 I / speak Spanish / not Japanese.
___
8 She / swim very far / not underwater.
___

PRONUNCIATION

can/can't: /æ/ and /ə/

A Listen and write *a*, *b* or *c* to show the correct sound for the underlined words.

a	/ə/
b	/æ/

Woman: OK. What [1]can you do? ____
Man: I [2]can climb. ____
Woman: Great. [3]Can you dive? ____
Man: Yes, I [4]can. ____
Woman: Fantastic! One more thing. [5]Can you drive? ____
Man: No, I [6]can't. Sorry. ____

B Listen again and repeat.

C Listen and underline *can* or *can't*.

1 I *can* / *can't* ski.
2 I *can* / *can't* speak Spanish.
3 I *can* / *can't* drive a car.
4 I *can* / *can't* hear you.
5 I *can* / *can't* climb.
6 I *can* / *can't* swim.

VOCABULARY

Abilities

A Complete the table with the words in the box.

a bicycle a cake a horse an omelette Chinese French Spanish tennis the guitar the piano

Make	Play

Ride	Speak

B Choose the correct options to complete the sentences.

1 We often *make* / *ski* in the mountains.
2 I like to *paint* / *play* pictures on the weekends.
3 Can you *talk* / *speak* Chinese?
4 Can you *drive* / *ride* a bicycle?
5 On my birthday, I have a party at home and we all listen to music and *ski* / *dance*.
6 I can *cook* / *draw* some easy meals, but nothing difficult!
7 Do you know how to *make* / *do* a cake?
8 I can *sing* / *say* and play the guitar.

C Complete the sentences with the words in the box.

do drive juggle paint plays rides sing speak

1 Can you ____________ the wall?
2 Can you ____________ a song in French?
3 I can't ____________ a bus.
4 Alison ____________ the drums.
5 Eric ____________ his horse on the weekends.
6 How many languages can you ____________?
7 We can't ____________ yoga!
8 Can you ____________ these three balls?

VOCABULARY
Adjectives

A Look at the puzzle and find 12 adjectives. The first two have been done for you.

w	f	g	n	i	r	p	p	d	o	a	r	s	h	o	r	t	a	s	p
s	v	a	a	w	w	u	f	e	l	x	a	i	a	s	e	e	r	p	e
e	t	i	n	t	e	r	e	s	t	i	n	g	u	g	a	d	e	e	f
r	i	e	e	r	b	b	n	f	j	z	a	e	i	f	p	q	e	a	f
s	i	g	r	e	a	t	m	b	y	a	i	e	m	g	u	u	d	s	s
y	m	n	e	a	a	b	s	c	m	c	n	g	o	o	d	s	t	y	o
o	l	k	s	t	y	u	i	a	d	d	m	s	n	f	p	o	g	y	i
u	y	u	s	s	r	r	p	s	i	e	o	x	n	s	i	o	x	t	i
n	e	d	o	o	l	d	p	c	f	r	s	b	e	e	i	e	j	s	n
g	m	i	g	l	l	e	a	t	f	h	d	o	r	e	r	l	m	t	g
i	n	t	f	a	w	f	w	h	i	m	h	r	p	o	e	o	n	b	b
n	e	r	h	e	i	l	n	m	c	e	j	i	s	p	p	n	f	v	a
g	a	w	f	u	l	t	n	i	u	r	k	n	e	y	n	g	q	e	d
n	n	m	h	u	t	r	a	f	l	b	r	g	t	t	a	h	a	i	d
d	i	f	n	m	w	a	v	k	t	e	d	o	p	q	s	s	z	e	r

1 *great*
2 *awful*
3 ______
4 ______
5 ______
6 ______
7 ______
8 ______
9 ______
10 ______
11 ______
12 ______

B Organize the adjectives you found in Exercise A into pairs of opposites.

great	*awful*
______	______
______	______
______	______
______	______
______	______

C Read the sentences and check (✓) the correct one in each pair.

1 a They are young musicians. ☐
  b They are youngs musicians. ☐
2 a It's a interesting book. ☐
  b It's an interesting book. ☐
3 a These questions are difficults. ☐
  b These questions are difficult. ☐
4 a This is a long movie! ☐
  b This is a movie long! ☐
5 a Their new song is great. ☐
  b Their new song is a great. ☐
6 a He is a bad dancer. ☐
  b He is an bad dancer. ☐

D Complete the text with the adjectives in the box.

amazing boring interesting talented terrible young

Bringing people TOGETHER

We are a group of friends and family who all enjoy music. We meet on the weekends and play music together. One or two people in the band are fantastic musicians and they're very [1] ______, but the others only do it for fun. Our singer is my son, Kyle. He's very [2] ______ (he's only 12), but he's an [3] ______ singer. I play the guitar, but I don't sing because Kyle says I'm [4] ______! When we meet, we don't always play music; sometimes we talk about it, too, and learn new things about different musicians, and that's really [5] ______. So you can see it's never [6] ______ when we get together!

He's amazing!

GRAMMAR
Possessive 's

A Choose the correct options to complete the sentences.

1 You know my sister Gina? This is my *sister friend* / *sister's friend* / *sisters' friend*, Anna.
2 My *brothers'* / *brother's* / *brothers* names are Ben and Carl.
3 I want to see Marcus. Where is *Marcus's* / *Marcus* / *Marcu's* office, please?
4 His *parent's* / *parents's* / *parents'* names are Celia and Frederik.
5 Simon is *Harry* / *Harrys's* / *Harry's* brother.
6 We go to work in my *colleague's* / *colleague* / *colleagues'* car. She's named Jan.
7 We have meetings in the *manager's office* / *managers office's* / *managers' office* because she has a big room and a nice view.
8 I sometimes stay at *Dannys* / *Dannys'* / *Danny's* house for the weekend.

B Add ' in the correct place in the words in bold.

1 I sometimes go to my **sons** school to talk to his teachers.
2 **Dinas** colleagues work in different cities around the world.
3 **Shes** been living with her two cousins.
4 Her **names** Nicole, but we call her Nicky.
5 Come and stay at my **parents** house in the countryside. My parents are wonderful!
6 Tonight is our **daughters** school concert – Darya plays the piano and Bahar sings.
7 The new **armchairs** gray with a blue cushion on it.
8 **Ollys sisters** names are Octavia and Maria.

C Read the sentences in Exercise B again. Is ' in each sentence *is*, *has* or possessive *'s* or *s'*?

1 ______
2 ______
3 ______
4 ______
5 ______
6 ______
7 ______
8 ______

PRONUNCIATION
Possessive 's

A Read the conversation and decide how we say the *'s* at the end of each underlined phrase. Write /z/, /s/ or /ɪz/.

Man: Excuse me. Is this [1]Amina's desk? ___
Woman: No, it isn't. This is [2]Bert's desk. ___
Man: So … is that one over there the desk I want?
Woman: No, that's [3]Marcus's desk. ___
Man: So, um …?
Woman: It's over there – next to the [4]manager's office. ___
Man: OK. Thanks a lot.
Woman: You're welcome.

7.3 **B Listen to the conversation from Exercise A and check your answers.**

READING

A PREPARE TO READ Look at the pictures. Which two activities can you see?

Activities with a DIFFERENCE

People come to Camp No Limits from all over the United States. At Camp No Limits, children and young people can climb, swim, play sports and ride horses. But there's something unusual about Camp No Limits – many of the campers can't walk or run. They love this camp because they can do things here which are difficult for them in everyday life.

Lauren comes to the activity camp for one week every summer. 'I'm 17 years old and I'm from Orlando, Florida. I can walk, but it's difficult and I get tired. Here at Camp No Limits, I play team sports like basketball every morning. Then, in the afternoon, I do my favorite activity – I ride a horse. I have a special teacher who helps me to get onto my horse – Harvey – and who rides with me. We go into the countryside and see beautiful trees, flowers and lakes. It's amazing!'

Yousef loves water sports. 'This is my first time at Camp No Limits and I love it! At my college, the only sports are soccer and basketball and I can't do those. Here, I can go swimming and diving in a special pool where I feel safe. The other people here are nice and friendly and now I have a lot of new friends, too. In the afternoon, I rest and then I meet my friends. We can paint and draw if we want, and there are photography classes, too. I want to come here every year!'

B READ FOR MAIN IDEA Read the first paragraph of *Activities with a difference* and choose the correct options to complete the sentences.

1 Camp No Limits is *for young people* / *only for small children*.

2 In their everyday life, they *usually* / *don't usually* do activities like swimming or climbing.

C READ FOR DETAIL Read the rest of the article and complete the sentences with one or two words in each blank.

1 Lauren usually stays at camp for ____________.

2 Lauren plays ____________ sports in the mornings.

3 For Lauren, the best thing about summer camp is that she can ____________ a horse.

4 Yousef ____________ play soccer or basketball.

5 He feels ____________ in the special swimming pool.

6 He would like to visit Camp No Limits ____________.

D REFLECT Think about the answers to these questions.

1 Is there a place like this near where you live?

2 What sports can you play?

LISTENING

A PREPARE TO LISTEN What are the main languages people speak in these countries?

1 Canada
2 Britain
3 Mexico
4 Morocco

7.4 **B LISTEN FOR GIST** Listen to the conversation between Rachel and Manu. Choose the correct options to complete the sentences.

1 Rachel speaks *two* / *three* languages.

2 Manu speaks *four* / *five* languages.

7.4 **C LISTEN FOR DETAIL** Listen again. Match the sentences (1–6) to the languages and places (a–f).

1 Rachel's homework is in this language.
2 Manu's grandparents live here.
3 Manu's grandparents speak this language.
4 Manu's father is from this country.
5 Manu's parents live here.
6 Manu's mother speaks these languages.

a Arabic
b Mexico
c Canada
d French, Arabic and Spanish
e French
f Morocco

D REFLECT Think about the answers to these questions.

1 How many languages can you speak?

2 Is it important to speak many languages? Why/Why not?

FUNCTIONAL LANGUAGE

Making polite requests

A Reorder the words to make a conversation.

A: [1]Mark's Hair / that / is / Hello,

_______________________________________?

B: Yes, it is.

A: [2]make / like / I'd / please / an appointment, / to

_______________________________________.

B: Sure. When do you want to come?

A: [3]time / Do / today / have / you

_______________________________________?

B: Yes. What time would you like to come?

A: [4]OK / two o'clock / Is

_______________________________________?

B: Yes, sure. See you then.

B Which sentence is more polite? Choose the best options.

1 **a** I want short hair, please.
  b I'd like short hair, please.

2 **a** Would you like a new hairstyle?
  b Do you want a new hairstyle?

C Choose the best options to complete the conversation.

Amal: Hi. Is this Sonja's Salon?

Sonja: Yes, it is. How [1]*can / would* I help you?

Amal: [2]*I'd want / I'd like* to make an appointment, please.

Sonja: [3]*Yes, of course. / It's OK.* When [4]*do you like / would you like* to come?

Amal: [5]*Do you have / Do you want* time this morning?

Sonja: Uh … let me see. Yes, that's [6]*right / fine*. What time [7]*would you like / is it*?

Amal: [8]*Is 11:30 OK / Is it 11:30*?

Sonja: Yes, 11:30 is good. See you then.

Amal: That's great! Thanks.

5 **D** Listen and check your answers to Exercise C.

WRITING

A Read the competition entry and answer the questions.

1 How old is Leila?

2 Where's she from?

3 What can she do?

- speak languages ☐
- ride a horse ☐
- play music ☐
- cook ☐
- dance ☐

Anyone Can Do It!

Name: Leila Risq **Age:** 22

About you: I'm Leila and I'm from Egypt. My father is Egyptian and my mother is Italian. I can [1]__________ Arabic Italian and English. I really love music. I can sing and [2]__________ the guitar violin and [3]__________. I like to cook as well. I can cook amazing [4]__________ from different parts of the world. My favorite [5]__________ is Italian, but I like Spanish Mexican Lebanese and Chinese, too.

B Complete Leila's competition entry with the words in the box.

drums	food	meals	play	speak

C **USING COMMAS IN LISTS** Read Leila's entry again and add the missing commas.

WRITING PRACTICE

A **PLAN** You are going to write a competition entry for someone you know who has many skills.

- Who is the person?
- How old are they?
- What can they do?
- Why are they talented?

B **WRITE** Write the competition entry. Use Leila's example to help you. Remember to use commas when you write a list of more than two items.

GRAMMAR
Present progressive

A Rewrite the verbs in the *-ing* form.

1 do ______
2 live ______
3 get ______
4 watch ______
5 sit ______
6 have ______
7 talk ______
8 meet ______
9 go ______
10 work ______
11 take ______
12 leave ______

B Use the prompts to write sentences in the present progressive. Use contractions.

1 He / not watch TV / listen to the radio.
He's not watching TV. He's listening to the radio.
2 They / play tennis / not play soccer.
______
3 We / wait at the station.
______
4 You / not listen to me.
______
5 I / take a nap.
______
6 She / drink coffee.
______

C Complete the short answers.

1 **A:** Are you enjoying the play, Sarah?
B: Yes, ______.
2 **A:** Is Steve doing yoga right now?
B: No, ______.
3 **A:** Are you and I going the right way?
B: Yes, ______.
4 **A:** Are they talking to someone?
B: No, ______.
5 **A:** Is Vicky going to the theater?
B: Yes, ______.
6 **A:** So, you're alone at home. Are you watching TV?
B: No, ______.
7 **A:** Are the children getting ready for the party?
B: Yes, ______.
8 **A:** Is it raining?
B: No, ______.

D Read the sentences. Then write questions using the question words in parentheses.

1 They're going to the movie theater. (*Where?*)
Where are they going?
2 I'm talking to my colleague. (*Who?*)
______
3 We're waiting for Jim at the café. (*Where?*)
______
4 She's meeting her friend at nine o'clock. (*When?*)
______
5 I'm going home because I'm cold. (*Why?*)
______
6 He's reading the newspaper. (*What?*)
______

E Complete the text with the present progressive form of the verb in parentheses. Use contractions if possible.

Right now, I'm at home. I [1] ______ (*not work*) today because it's Saturday. I [2] ______ (*cook*) lunch for my family. My wife and my daughter [3] ______ (*shop*) in town. They [4] ______ (*look*) for something for my daughter to wear to a party tonight. My son's here with me. He [5] ______ (*do*) his English homework. He [6] ______ (*also / listen*) to his favorite band, and now he [7] ______ (*sing*). Outside it's cold, but at least it [8] ______ (*not rain*).

8.1 The here and now

What's he doing?

VOCABULARY
Verb phrases

A Choose the correct options to complete the sentences.

1 I'm *having* / *going* shopping.
2 We're *talking* / *meeting* Jenny at the station.
3 Let's *take* / *make* a selfie!
4 He's *looking* / *reading* at his phone again!
5 We're *having* / *taking* lunch in a restaurant today.
6 I sometimes *look at* / *watch* TV in the evenings.
7 She's *reading* / *looking* the newspaper.
8 We frequently *meet* / *talk* on the phone.

B Complete the sentences with the correct form of the verbs in the box.

go have look meet read take talk watch

1 I usually ________________ my friends at our favorite café.
2 Why are you ________________ in the mirror?
3 Can you ________________ good photos on your phone?
4 Let's go out tonight and ________________ a good time.
5 She's ________________ the messages on her phone.
6 I like to sit at a café and ________________ the people go by.
7 When do you usually ________________ to the bank?
8 Do you want to ________________ about your problem?

PRONUNCIATION
Different ways to pronounce *a*

8.1 **A** Listen and complete the sentences.

1 How often do you ________________ TV?
2 Who are you ________________ to?
3 Do you ________________ a lot of photos?
4 Do you ________________ tennis every weekend?
5 Tom ________________ the car on Sundays.
6 Be careful! That tree is ________________!
7 Remember to ________________ your parents.
8 Patti is ________________ with her grandmother this week.
9 Hurry up! I need to ________________ the bus.

B Add the words you wrote in Exercise A to the correct place in the table.

/æ/	/eɪ/	/ɔː/	/ɑ/

VOCABULARY
Clothes

A Look at the pictures and complete the paragraphs with one word in each blank. The first letter is given to help you.

The best of **FASHION WEEK!**

Dan is wearing a [1]c__________ and sunglasses. He's wearing a cool white [2]T-__________ with a picture of headphones on it. He isn't wearing pants – he's wearing [3]s__________. He's also wearing black [4]s__________.

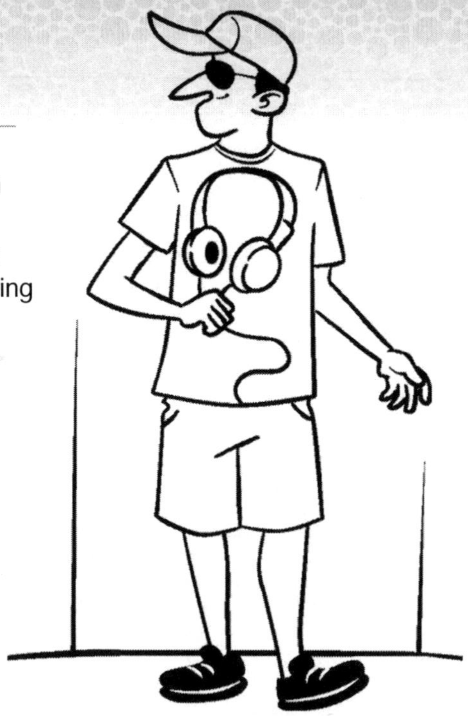

Kaydee has a big, black [5]h__________ on – it's really amazing! She's wearing a white [6]d__________. She's wearing white [7]s__________ and black and white [8]s__________.

B Choose the correct options to complete the sentences.

1. It's cold outside. You need a ___.
   - **a** shorts
   - **b** coat
2. You always wear the same jeans! Do you have any other ___?
   - **a** pants
   - **b** sneakers
3. I want to look good at work, so I always wear a ___.
   - **a** T-shirt
   - **b** suit
4. Annie is looking for a new ___ to wear to her friend's party.
   - **a** pants
   - **b** skirt
5. He's wearing a white ___ and a brown jacket.
   - **a** shirt
   - **b** shorts
6. Petros is wearing a ___ because it's cold today.
   - **a** T-shirt and shorts
   - **b** sweater and coat
7. You don't wear ___ to an important meeting – you wear a suit.
   - **a** jeans
   - **b** a shirt
8. I like those ___ – they are a nice color.
   - **a** jacket
   - **b** shoes
9. It's my birthday party this weekend and I need a new ___.
   - **a** shoes
   - **b** dress
10. My favorite ___ is black and white.
    - **a** shorts
    - **b** sweater

C Circle the odd word out in each group.

1. socks / shoes / sneakers / (cap)
2. cap / shorts / hat / sunglasses
3. dress / pants / shorts / jeans
4. shirt / sweater / jacket / skirt
5. pants / skirt / shirt / shorts

The gray coat

PRONUNCIATION

Vowel sounds: /iː/, /ɜː/, /uː/ and /ɔː/

A Match the underlined letters in the sentences (1–4) to the sounds (a–d). Use each sound only once.

1 Who do you know at the party? ____
2 What's the word for this part of a bird? ____
3 Let's walk and talk. ____
4 Is my green shirt clean? ____

a /iː/ (like *jeans*)
b /ɜː/ (like *shirt*)
c /uː/ (like *shoes*)
d /ɔː/ (like *law or shorts*)

B Listen to the sentences from Exercise A. Then practice saying them in the same way as the speakers in the recording.

C Connect the words with the /iː/ sound to get out of the maze.

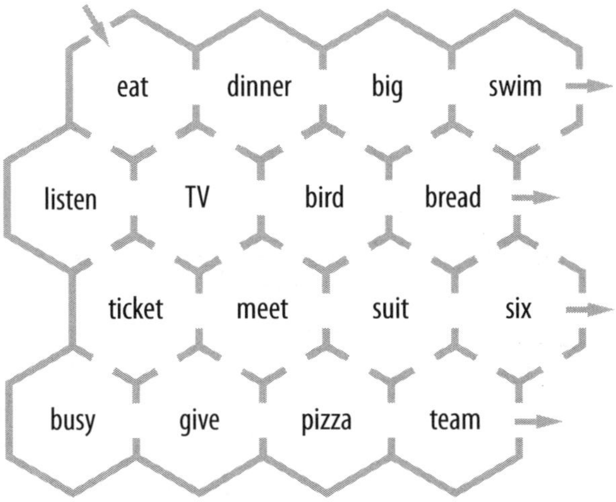

D Connect the words with the /ɔː/ sound to get out of the maze.

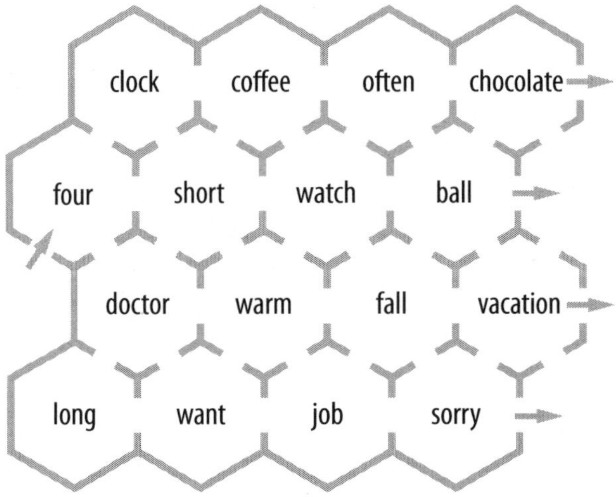

GRAMMAR

Adjective order

A Complete the sentences with the adjectives in parentheses in the correct order.

1 She has a ________ ________ hat. (*new / green*)
2 Francois has a ________ ________ coat. (*blue / long*)
3 I like this ________ ________ jacket. What do you think? (*gray / short*)
4 There's a ________ ________ coat on the chair. (*long / yellow*)
5 Look at his ________ ________ sneakers! (*white / new*)
6 He's wearing a(n) ________ ________ T-shirt. (*old / gray*)
7 He wants a ________ ________ T-shirt. (*blue / big*)
8 I have a(n) ________ ________ sweater that I love! (*great / old*)

B Check (✓) the correct sentences and put an (✗) for the incorrect sentences.

1 Do you like old big houses? ☐
2 Where is my new white shirt? ☐
3 She's wearing her orange new pants. ☐
4 Is Viv the girl with long brown hair? ☐
5 I'd like a black large coffee, please. ☐
6 There's a black small table in the room. ☐
7 Sia has gray short hair and blue eyes. ☐
8 Dad always wears a long green coat in the yard. ☐

READING

A SCAN FOR INFORMATION Read the email quickly and answer the questions with one word.

1 Who wrote the email?
2 Who are they writing to?
3 Are they friends or colleagues?

Re: Traveling for business
To: Jo.Radford@hemail.net
From: KenB@e-solutions.net

Hi Jo,

I'm sorry, but I can't come to your birthday party. I'm in China right now. I'm working at our office in Shanghai this week. I'm teaching my Chinese colleagues how to use the company's new computer program. They're very friendly, they speak perfect English and they're learning really quickly. Shanghai is a fantastic city and the work isn't difficult, so I'm having a good time here.

After work, I walk around the city, or I sit in the sun at the park and relax. This afternoon, it's raining, so I'm staying inside at the hotel. It's a big new hotel in the city center and I have a nice room with a view of the river. Right now, I'm reading my emails and listening to music. Sometimes I meet one of my colleagues in the evening and we go out for dinner.

I'm back home on Sunday morning. Do you want to come over to my house in the afternoon? I have something for your birthday.

Have a great time tomorrow, and Happy Birthday! Say hi to everybody from me.

Ken

B READ FOR KEY WORDS Read the email again and complete the summary with one word in each blank.

Ken is in [1]________, China, for work, so he can't go to Jo's birthday [2]________. He's staying in a nice [3]________ and his [4]________ are friendly. He wants to see Jo on [5]________ afternoon.

C READ FOR DETAIL Read the email again. Are the sentences true (T) or false (F)?

1 Ken is teaching his colleagues to speak English. T / F
2 Ken is happy to be in Shanghai for work. T / F
3 It's warm and sunny every day. T / F
4 Ken's hotel room has a view of the city center. T / F
5 Right now, he's having his dinner. T / F
6 Jo's birthday is tomorrow. T / F

D REFLECT Think about the answers to these questions.

1 Do you travel for work? Where do you go?
2 Do you like visiting new places?

LISTENING

A PREPARE TO LISTEN Look at the two pictures. What is the difference between the dog in Picture 1 and the dog in Picture 2?

1

2

8.3 **B LISTEN FOR GIST** Listen to a conversation and answer the questions.

1 How many differences are there between the two pictures?
2 Do the speakers find all the differences?
3 Why does the woman leave?

8.3 **C LISTEN FOR DETAIL** Listen again, look at the pictures and circle the differences you hear. Which difference do they not find?

D REFLECT Think about the answers to these questions.

1 Do you enjoy playing games like this?
2 What other games or competitions do you like?

FUNCTIONAL LANGUAGE

Shopping for clothes

A Listen to a conversation. Are the sentences true (T) or
4 false (F)?

1. Lauren is looking for a T-shirt. *T / F*
2. Grace wants a medium size. *T / F*
3. The store doesn't have T-shirts in Grace's size. *T / F*
4. Lauren doesn't like the red T-shirt. *T / F*
5. Grace buys the blue one. *T / F*

B Reorder the words to make sentences and questions.

1. it / How / is / much
______________________________?
2. them / a lot / have / We / of
______________________________.
3. color / What / you / like / would
______________________________?
4. for / She's / T-shirt / looking / a
______________________________.
5. you / help / I / Can
______________________________?

C Complete the conversation with the phrases from
4 Exercise B. Then listen and check.

Lauren: Hey, Grace. That store has what you want.
Grace: It does? OK, let's go there.
Assistant: Good morning. [1] ______________________?
Grace: We're just looking, thanks.
Lauren: Hold on, Grace. Actually, [2] ______________________.
Assistant: Of course. [3] ______________________.
What size would you like?
Grace: Small, please.
Assistant: No problem. And [4] ______________________?
Grace: Do you have a red one?
Assistant: Is this one OK?
Grace: Hmm. It's not bad. Lauren, what do you think?
Lauren: I think it's horrible. Buy the blue one.
Grace: OK. [5] ______________________?
Assistant: $15.
Grace: Thanks, I'll take it.

WRITING

A Read the text message conversation. Correct the sentences.

1. Olly is sitting in the park.
Olly is shopping.
2. He's alone.
____
3. Tessa is buying a hat.
____
4. Jasmine is shopping, too.
____

What's everyone doing?

Hi Jasmine. I'm shopping. I'm buying a hat and some new shoes, [1] ______________.

Hi Olly. Cool. Are you alone?

No! Hi! It's me, Tessa. 🙂 Gerry's here, [2] ______________.

Are you [3] ______________ buying shoes, Tessa? I know you love shoes!

No. They're waiting for me, then we're going to the park. Do you want to come?

I'd love to, but I can't. I'm studying right now. [4] ______________, it's my mom's birthday tomorrow, so I need to buy her a present.

OK. Maybe next time.

B Read the conversation again. Complete the messages with *too* or *also*.

WRITING PRACTICE

WRITE You are going to write a text message conversation between three friends. Use the conversation in Exercise B and the picture to help you. Remember to use *too* and *also*.

GRAMMAR
Simple past: *was/were*

A Complete the text with the words in the box.

was (x2) wasn't Were were (x3) weren't

Vincent van Gogh

Vincent van Gogh was born in the Netherlands in 1853. His parents [1] ______ fairly rich, but Vincent [2] ______ rich when he died at the age of 37. He [3] ______ a great artist, but his paintings [4] ______ popular in his lifetime. [5] ______ they bad paintings? Certainly not, but it [6] ______ a long time before people [7] ______ interested in them. Later, they [8] ______ very expensive – and today, they cost millions!

B Read the text and write questions for the underlined answers in the text.

Frida Kahlo

[1]Frida Kahlo was born in Mexico City on July 6, 1907. [2]She was a great artist. [3]At first, her paintings weren't popular – maybe [4]they were too modern! [5]Later, they were very popular. They are in art museums all over the world and they cost millions of dollars. [6]Many of her paintings were pictures of herself. Were they the first selfies?

1 **A:** *Was Frida Kahlo born in Mexico City?*
B: Yes, she was.

2 **A:** ______
B: Yes, she was.

3 **A:** ______
B: No, they weren't.

4 **A:** ______
B: Yes, they were.

5 **A:** ______
B: Yes, they were.

6 **A:** ______
B: Yes, they were.

VOCABULARY
Dates and years

A **Choose the correct options to complete the sentences.**

1 Let's go to the New York Film Festival on March *thirtieth / thirty*.

2 The Empire State Building in New York is from the *one thousand nine / nineteen* thirties.

3 Art Deco was popular in New York in the *twenties / twentieth* century.

4 Today, in the *twenty-one / twenty-first* century, more than 8,600,000 people live in New York City.

5 The Tower Building (1889) was the *first / one* skyscraper in New York.

B **Write the numbers in words.**

1 He was a writer in the 16th century.

______

2 I was born in 1990.

______

3 Today is December 12th.

______

4 I wasn't with this company in 2002.

______

5 Was that in 1909?

______

6 Is August the 7th or 8th month of the year?

______

7 Shakespeare was born in 1564.

______

PRONUNCIATION
was he / was she

9.1 **A** **Read the questions. Then listen and check (✓) if what you hear is the same as the written question. Rewrite the questions that are different.**

1 Was he the US president? ______

2 Was she a painter? ______

3 Where was he born? ______

4 Was he tired? ______

5 Why was she famous? ______

6 What year was she born? ______

7 Was he OK in the lesson? ______

8 Who was she with? ______

9.1 **B** **Listen again and repeat the questions. Copy the linked words.**

VOCABULARY
Everyday verbs

A Complete the short conversations with the verbs in the box.

collect design help paint receive start study travel

1 **A:** Do you ________________ at college?
B: No, I'm an architect. I ________________ buildings.

2 **A:** Do you often ________________ presents? What were these flowers for?
B: I sometimes ________________ a friend with her work. These are to say 'Thank you'.

3 **A:** Do you have a hobby? Do you ________________ stamps, for example?
B: No, I don't, but I sometimes like to ________________ pictures.

4 **A:** What time does your day ________________?
B: Very early – I have to ________________ to New York every morning.

B Complete the crossword with the correct form of the verbs in Exercise A.

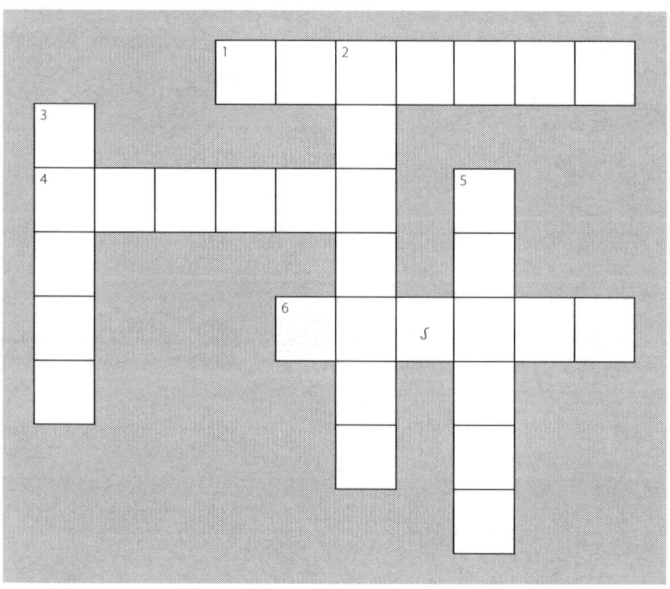

Across

1 I love to give presents, but I also love to ________________ them!

4 How far do you ________________ to work every day?

6 I want to ________________ cell phones. I have a lot of good ideas for new ones.

Down

2 A lot of children ________________ stamps, but not many people over the age of 16 do.

3 It's expensive to ________________ at college in New York.

5 Nikki ________________ pictures at home to relax.

C Choose the correct options to complete the descriptions.

Dorothy Vaughan (1910–2008)

Vaughan was a mathematician. She was born in Kansas City in the US. She [1]***started / studied*** mathematics at college. In 1943, she got a job at the Langley Research Center. She worked there for the next 28 years and [2]***started / traveled*** to work every day by public transportation. In 1949, she became the first African–American woman to lead a team. She was an important part of the NASA space program.

Carson McCullers (1917–1967)

McCullers was a writer. She was born in Georgia in the US. When she was 10, she [3]***started / studied*** to learn the piano. In 1934, she moved to New York to study music. However, she got very sick and decided to be a writer instead. In 1940, she [4]***collected / received*** $500 for her first story, *The Heart Is a Lonely Hunter*. Many of her stories were turned into plays and movies.

Elsa Schiaparelli (1890–1973)

Schiaparelli was a fashion designer. She was born in Rome in Italy. In 1922, she moved to France and began making clothes. In the 1930s, she [5]***designed / painted*** the 'wrap dress' which is still famous today. In 1934, Salvador Dalí [6]***helped / studied*** her design the 'Lobster Dress'. She also designed costumes for movies.

GRAMMAR

Simple past: regular verbs

A **Complete the table with the correct simple past forms of the verbs in the box.**

ask circle complete cry ~~decide~~ paint start ~~study~~ try

Add *-d*	Add *-ed*	Cut the *-y*, add *-ied*
decided	asked	studied

B **Choose the correct options to complete the sentences.**

1 We ***received*** / ***receive*** your letter yesterday.
2 Sandra didn't ***want*** / ***wanted*** to be a dancer.
3 I ***not looked*** / ***didn't look*** at my phone all day today.
4 Khanh ***studyed*** / ***studied*** at college for three years.
5 I ***started*** / ***start*** piano lessons last summer.
6 We didn't ***studied*** / ***study*** Spanish at our school.
7 She ***cry*** / ***cried*** when she heard the news.
8 Chantelle ***designed*** / ***did design*** the house together with an architect.

C **Complete the sentences with the simple past form of the verbs in parentheses.**

1 I ______________ my new Spanish course yesterday. (*start*)
2 We ______________ TV last night because there was nothing good on. (*not watch*)
3 My grandfather ______________ stamps when he was young. (*collect*)
4 His wife ______________ to Berlin for work last week. (*travel*)
5 He ______________ that picture – it was a professional artist! (*not paint*)
6 I ______________ to anyone yesterday. (*not talk*)
7 She ______________ to be a doctor when she was a child. (*want*)
8 They ______________ a great new café in the city center. (*discover*)
9 You ______________ me yesterday! (*not call*)
10 I ______________ over 200 emails yesterday – it was awful! (*receive*)

PRONUNCIATION

Past tense endings: /d/, /t/ and /ɪd/

9.2 **A** **Listen and circle the verb in parentheses whose ending sounds the same as the underlined verb.**

1 We <u>wanted</u> to go home. (***asked*** / ***decided*** / ***lived***)
2 He <u>traveled</u> for many years. (***designed*** / ***collected*** / ***looked***)
3 He <u>asked</u> for some money. (***started*** / ***traveled*** / ***helped***)
4 They <u>started</u> to run. (***talked*** / ***designed*** / ***collected***)
5 We <u>studied</u> in Italy. (***collected*** / ***cried*** / ***asked***)
6 She <u>collected</u> stamps when she was young. (***wanted*** / ***helped*** / ***asked***)

9.3 **B** **Choose the correct ending sounds for the <u>underlined</u> verbs. Then listen and check.**

1 We <u>played</u> soccer until it got dark. /d/ /t/ /ɪd/
2 The receptionist <u>looked</u> at me and smiled. /d/ /t/ /ɪd/
3 I really <u>needed</u> your help yesterday! /d/ /t/ /ɪd/
4 They <u>painted</u> the house a different color. /d/ /t/ /ɪd/
5 I <u>cleaned</u> the kitchen, then went to bed. /d/ /t/ /ɪd/
6 She <u>worked</u> in New York for 10 years. /d/ /t/ /ɪd/

9.3 **C** **Listen again and repeat the sentences.**

READING

A READ FOR GIST Read *Everyday hero* quickly. What is the main topic of the article?

- science
- education
- art
- technology

B READ FOR GIST Read the article again. Match the headings (a–c) with the main paragraphs (1–3).

a Working for the future ____
b Early life ____
c School and studies ____

C READ FOR SPECIFIC INFORMATION Read the article again and complete the information.

Name: 1 ____________
Country: 2 ____________
Born in: 3 ____________
Opened a: 4 ____________

Everyday HERO

We frequently think of heroes as famous men or women from the past. Kakenya Ntaiya isn't famous and she isn't a scientist or a politician, but she *is* a hero!

[1] Kakenya was born in Kenya in 1978. Her traditional life in East Africa was hard work. When she was a child, her day started at 5 am. She cooked food for her seven brothers and sisters and collected water for the family. She dreamed of a different life – she wanted to become a teacher.

[2] So, Kakenya studied hard at school and received a spot at an American university, but her family wanted her to stay at home and have a family. Finally, they agreed and she traveled to the US to begin her studies.

[3] Some years later, she returned to her village and asked the women, 'What do you need?' They said that they wanted a school for their daughters. In May 2009, Kakenya opened the 'Kakenya Center for Excellence' in her village. Today, hundreds of girls at her school study English, Swahili, science, social science and math there. They also learn about nature, traditional music and dance and play safely in the schoolyard. Kakenya received many prizes and awards for her work. 'I want to make our tomorrow better', she says.

D READ FOR SPECIFIC INFORMATION Read the article again and choose the correct options to complete the sentences.

1 The writer thinks Kakenya is a ***hero / famous person***.
2 She ***worked / didn't work*** hard when she was a young girl.
3 Kakenya ***didn't study / studied*** in the US.
4 Kakenya's school is ***for girls and boys / only for girls***.
5 She thinks that ***the past / the future*** is important.

E REFLECT Think about the answers to these questions.

1 What do you think makes someone a hero?
2 Do girls receive the same education as boys in your country?

LISTENING

A PREPARE TO LISTEN Read the questions in Exercise C. What do you think you will hear about in the listening?

1 famous writers
2 famous painters
3 famous writers and painters

9.4 **B LISTEN FOR GIST** Listen to the quiz. How much money does Tom win?

9.4 **C LISTEN FOR SPECIFIC INFORMATION** Listen again and choose the correct options (a, b or c) to answer the questions.

1 What nationality was the painter Claude Monet?
a Spanish b French c Belgian

2 When was the painter Pablo Picasso born?
a 1875 b 1894 c 1881

3 What was the language of Joseph Conrad's books?
a Polish b English c French

4 What was the name of Andy Warhol's style of art?
a pop art b selfie-art c world art

5 Which writer studied to become a doctor?
a Michael Crichton
b Margaret Atwood
c Stephen King

D REFLECT Think about the answers to these questions.

1 Do you enjoy quizzes? Why/Why not?
2 What 'special subject' would you choose on a quiz show?

FUNCTIONAL LANGUAGE
Making recommendations

A Listen to a conversation between friends and answer the questions.

1 What kind of food does Izzie want to eat?

____

2 How many restaurants does Dev know for that type of food?

____

3 What two things are wrong with the first restaurant Dev suggests?

____

4 What is wrong with the second restaurant Dev suggests?

____

5 Does Izzie want to go to the third restaurant he suggests? Why/Why not?

____

B Complete the conversation with the words and phrases in the box.

Are there	Don't	know	should	Why don't you	wouldn't

Izzie: Do you [1] ______________ any good restaurants around here?

Dev: Yes, I do. What do you like? Indian food? Japanese? Italian?

Izzie: My favorite is Mexican food.

Dev: Let me see … There are three Mexican restaurants in town – I'll show you on the map. [2] ______________ go to this one – I was there on Saturday night and the food was terrible, *and* it wasn't cheap.

Izzie: OK.

Dev: Now this one isn't far, but I [3] ______________ go there, either. It's also too expensive.

Izzie: OK. And the third one?

Dev: Yes! You [4] ______________ definitely go to that one. It's my favorite!

Izzie: How do I get there?

Dev: Um. It's kind of far away. [5] ______________ take a taxi?

Izzie: [6] ______________ any other good, cheap restaurants nearby?

C Now listen to the conversation and check your answers to Exercise B.

WRITING

A Look at the picture above and answer the questions.

1 In which country do you think this building is located?

2 Do you know the name of this style of architecture?

B Read the short biography about Walter Gropius. Check your answers to Exercise A.

Walter Gropius

Walter Gropius was born in Berlin in Germany in 1883. He was a designer and architect. He designed and built his first buildings in 1910 when he was 27 years old. He is famous for starting the Bauhaus school of architecture and was also a teacher of art and design. He frequently worked with other architects. His most well-known building is the Bauhaus School in Dessau, Germany. He wanted it to be both useful and beautiful. He moved to the UK in 1934 and later to the US. He died there in 1969.

C **ORGANIZING YOUR NOTES** Read the biography again. Put the notes (a–f) in the order you read about them.

a famous building(s) ___
b birth place ___
c why famous ___
d occupation ___
e name ___
f birth date ___

WRITING PRACTICE

A **PLAN** You are going to write a short biography of the musician Louis Armstrong. Look at the picture and the notes. Decide on the best order for the information.

Name	:	*Louis Armstrong*
Famous song	:	*'What a wonderful world'*
Activities	:	*played trumpet and sang, acted in movies*
Birth place	:	*New Orleans*
Why famous?	:	*made jazz popular*
Occupation	:	*jazz musician*
Birth date	:	*1901*

B **WRITE** Write your biography. Use your notes and plan from Exercise A.

GRAMMAR

Simple past: irregular verbs

A Choose the correct options to complete the sentences.

1 Workers *found* / *finded* these important objects under the old house.

2 He didn't know what to do with the axe, so he *did give* / *gave* it to the museum.

3 I *wore* / *wear* my favorite jacket to dinner because it was a special evening.

4 People wrote letters in the past – they didn't *sent* / *send* emails.

5 It *taked* / *took* me two hours to get to work yesterday morning!

6 We *choose* / *chose* some nice flowers to give to Marcia.

7 Phil didn't *have* / *had* breakfast because he was late for work.

8 **A:** Do you have the same smartphone?
B: No, I *sold* / *did sell* it and *buyed* / *bought* a new one.

B Rewrite the sentences in the simple past. Use the words in parentheses to help you.

1 I go to the movie theater. (*last Saturday*)
I went to the movie theater last Saturday.

2 I wear jeans and a T-shirt. (*yesterday*)
______

3 I make a lot of phone calls. (*last week*)
______

4 They don't have breakfast at home. (*this morning*)
______

5 She writes a lot of emails. (*yesterday*)
______

6 You don't send many text messages. (*yesterday*)
______

7 He takes a lot of photographs on vacation. (*last summer*)
______

8 You buy a lot of new shoes! (*last week*)
______

9 I don't see you. (*yesterday*)
______

10 He gives her flowers! (*last Saturday*)
______

C Complete the text with the correct forms of the verbs in the box. The first letter is given to help you.

buy choose have make sell wear

About | Profile | Blog | Contact

What was it like?

In the 1950s and 60s, life in the US was very different from the way it is today. It was a time when men frequently [1]w______ suits, not just for work. They [2]c______ to wear them every day including the weekend! People also [3]m______ their own clothes, sometimes because they didn't [4]h______ the money to buy new things and sometimes because they wanted to. Only a few people [5]b______ radios, televisions and telephones and there were a lot of stores that didn't [6]s______ expensive things like that – people rented them instead and paid every week or every month.

VOCABULARY
Time phrases

A Complete the table with the words and phrases in the box to make past time expressions.

~~10 minutes~~ 20 years 100 years 1986 2002
a couple of minutes the 1990s ~~the 21st century~~
the past Tuesday two weeks week year

In	Ago	Last
the 21st century	*10 minutes*	

B One word is missing from each sentence. Write *in*, *ago* or *last* in the correct place.

1 I had dinner with my wife Friday.
2 The manager left an hour.
3 The company started 2018.
4 We didn't work week.
5 Someone made this snake the 15th century.
6 These people lived a long time.
7 I found this job year.
8 60 years, life was very different.

C Find and correct the mistakes in the time phrases in the sentences.

1 I went there before two years.
2 We had a meeting on last Friday.
3 They found the coins the last year.
4 The past, there were trains, but not many cars.
5 I spoke to Jim an hour before.
6 We had no work the past week.
7 You missed the class the last Tuesday.
8 We met five years past.

PRONUNCIATION
Vowel sounds: /ɔː/ and /oʊ/

A Match the <u>underlined</u> sounds in the sentences (1–5) to the sounds (a or b). Use each sound more than once.

1 I like to w<u>al</u>k and t<u>al</u>k to my friend. ___
2 I s<u>aw</u> a t<u>al</u>l man. ___
3 She b<u>ou</u>ght f<u>ou</u>r paintings. ___
4 He ch<u>o</u>se to g<u>o</u> al<u>o</u>ne. ___
5 We sh<u>ow</u>ed our h<u>o</u>me to the realtor. ___
6 I th<u>ou</u>ght he always w<u>o</u>re black. ___

a /ɔː/ (like *t<u>au</u>ght*)
b /oʊ/ (like *ph<u>o</u>ne*)

10.1 **B** Listen to the sentences from Exercise A. Then practice saying them in the same way as the speakers in the recording.

VOCABULARY
Life events

A Complete the crossword with the simple past form of the verbs.

Across

1 win
3 drive
5 get
6 finish
7 meet

Down

1 write
2 belong
4 pass

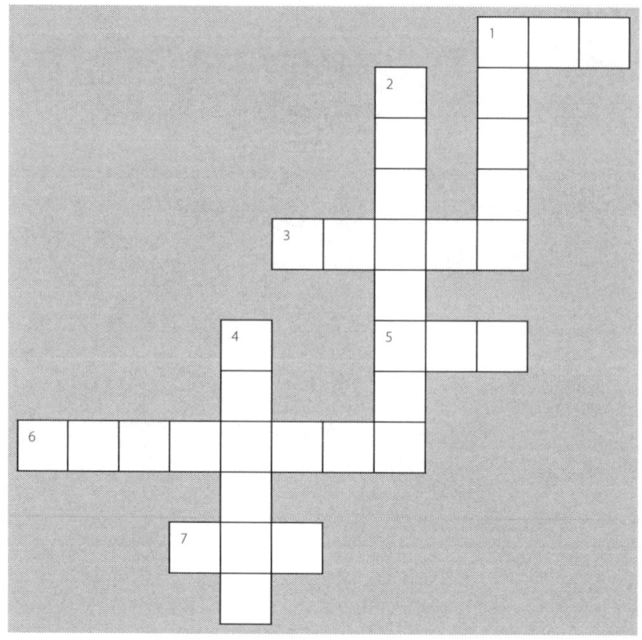

B Complete the text with the simple past verbs from Exercise A.

Times of our lives

In this series, we talk to people about the important moments in their lives. This week, we talk to Mark Berger, a businessman from Atlanta.

I enjoyed school when I was a child, especially my English classes. I remember that I [1] ________ a lot of stories, and I [2] ________ prizes for some of them in school competitions. I loved writing, and I wanted to become a writer then!

A very important moment for me was when I [3] ________ a car for the first time. The car [4] ________ to my dad. I was very nervous, but I loved it, and it was good to have my dad there with me. I was very happy when I [5] ________ my test, and I still love driving today.

Learning to drive was definitely an important moment in my life, but the most important day in my life was when I [6] ________ my wife, Lorraine, while we were both students studying in New York. We [7] ________ married after we [8] ________ college.

GRAMMAR
Simple past questions

A **Put *did* in the correct place in the questions.**

1 When they get married?
2 They get married in the spring?
3 Where the wedding take place?
4 What time it start?
5 How many people they invite?
6 Why they take this picture?
7 Who they ask to take it?
8 They have an amazing day?

B **Complete the short answers to the questions.**

1 **A:** Did your father buy this car last year?
B: No, ______________________.
2 **A:** Did your mother drive it, too?
B: Yes, ______________________.
3 **A:** Did the family use it every day?
B: No, ______________________.
4 **A:** Did it cost a lot of money?
B: Yes, ______________________.
5 **A:** Did you ever drive this car?
B: No, ______________________.

C **Write questions in the simple past. Use the question words in parentheses to help you.**

1 We met James outside the station. (*Where?*)
Where did you meet James?
2 I sent 27 emails yesterday. (*How many?*)
____
3 I finished the book last week. (*What?*)
____
4 My mother gave me this ring last year. (*When?*)
____
5 We left the movie theater because the movie was boring. (*Why?*)
____
6 The train arrived at six ten. (*When?*)
____
7 I called Samantha last night. (*Who?*)
____
8 I bought a new computer yesterday. (*What?*)
____
9 We went home because it started to rain. (*Why?*)
____
10 They sold eight paintings. (*How many?*)
____

PRONUNCIATION
Final consonant /t/ and /d/

10.2 **A** **Listen and choose the correct options to complete the sentences.**

1 How old were you when you learned to *ride* / *write*?
2 I *sent* / *send* a lot of emails.
3 Who *set* / *said* that?
4 I need a new *code* / *coat*.
5 They *built* / *build* a lot of new roads.
6 I *spend* / *spent* a lot of money.

10.2 **B** **Listen to the sentences from Exercise A again and repeat.**

A HISTORY OF TIME

You probably use your phone to tell the time and many people wear a watch for the same reason. But did you know that people first started counting time thousands of years ago?

Sundial

In ancient Egypt and Iraq, people used sundials to tell the time. The sun went across the sky and the sundial showed them the hour of the day. The Greeks and Romans used them, too. People used them until the early 19th century, so they were around for a very long time! There were small 'pocket' sundials, too.

Hourglass

In Europe in the 14th century, people used the hourglass to tell the time on boats. Every hour, they turned the glass and wrote the time in a book. They used these times to find out how fast and how far they traveled.

Clock

It wasn't until the end of the 13th century that somebody made the first clock. These clocks were very big and people built them in tall towers so everybody could see the time. The oldest working clock in the world is in a tower in Salisbury in the UK. It's from 1386.

Watch

People didn't have their own watches ('pocket watches') until the 16th century. But they were very expensive and only rich people had them. In the 1900s, they started making watches which were cheaper and soon everybody had one.

READING

A PREDICT Look at the pictures in *A history of time*. Which way of telling the time do you think is the oldest?

B READ FOR GIST Read the text. Choose the best summary of the main idea.

- **a** People didn't know how to tell the time until the 20th century when each person had their own watch.
- **b** People used different ways to tell the time, from an object which used the sun to modern watches and phones.

C READ FOR MAIN IDEA Read the text again and choose the correct options to complete the sentences.

1. Sundials were useful to people *only in the ancient world* / *for thousands of years*.
2. Sundials were *very big* / *big and small*.
3. In the 14th century, people on boats used an hourglass to calculate *time* / *time and distance*.
4. The first clocks were *in the UK* / *in towers*.
5. Watches were for everybody in the *1900s* / *1600s*.

D REFLECT Think about the answers to these questions.

1. Which information in the text was a surprise to you?
2. Why is it important to tell the time?

LISTENING

A PREDICT Look at the picture. Do you think this building is a theater, a museum or an art gallery?

B LISTEN FOR GIST (10.3) Listen to a conversation about a visit to the building in Exercise A and check your answer. Then write short answers to the questions.

1. Did the man enjoy his visit?
2. Did he only see metal objects?
3. Does the woman want to go there, too?

C LISTEN FOR DETAIL (10.3) Listen again and complete the sentences with one to three words in each blank.

1. The Victoria and Albert Museum is in ____________.
2. They built the museum ____________.
3. You can see objects related to ____________ at the museum.
4. The model boat had ____________ in it.
5. The man saw a ____________ which was like a snake.
6. The man ____________ see Princess Diana's wedding dress.
7. The man liked the toy tiger because tigers are ____________.
8. The model of the tiger is from ____________.

D REFLECT Think about the answers to these questions.

1. Which of the objects that the man talked about did you find most interesting?
2. Would you like to visit this museum? Why/Why not?

FUNCTIONAL LANGUAGE
Showing interest

A Match the sentences (1–5) to the responses (a–g). There are two extra responses.

1 She had a terrible weekend. ___
2 I went to a Jay-Z concert at the Arena with some friends. ___
3 I went to Rome with my brother. ___
4 I stayed at home and watched TV. ___
5 The food was bad. ___

a It was also interesting.
b That sounds awful.
c Nice! I love his music.
d Oh, what a shame. Why?
e Really? Wow! How cool! I love the buildings there.
f Where did you go?
g Sounds good. I like to relax on the weekends, too.

B Complete the conversation with the words in the box.

amazing enjoyed nice shame sounds talking terrible watched

Seb: Hi, Leila. How was your weekend?
Leila: Hi, Seb. Not good. I went shopping and bought some new headphones, and then guess what? I left them on the bus! In the evening, I went out for pizza with my parents, but it was [1] ________!
Seb: That [2] ________ awful. Oh look, here come Mike and Chris.
Mike: Hi guys. What are you [3] ________ about?
Seb: What we did over the weekend. Leila says she had a terrible weekend.
Mike: Oh. What a [4] ________. I went to New York City with my brother.
Leila: Really? Wow!
Chris: Yes, that sounds [5] ________.
Mike: Yes, it was. What did you do Chris?
Chris: I just stayed at home and [6] ________ soccer with some friends.
Leila: That's [7] ________. Was it a good game?
Chris: Yes, I really [8] ________ it. My team won.
Seb: I watched the game, too. It was a great game.

10.4 **C** Now listen and check your answers to Exercise B.

WRITING

A Read the story. Are the sentences true (T) or false (F)?

1 It was Jan's birthday yesterday. *T / F*
2 Jan had coffee before she went shopping. *T / F*
3 The police officer asked Jan personal information. *T / F*
4 Jan went shopping again later. *T / F*
5 Jan used the extra ticket to take Martha to the concert. *T / F*

About | **Submit** | Contact

Jan went shopping yesterday because she wanted to buy a birthday present for her friend, Martha. [1] ________ two hours of shopping, she went to a café. She found a table and ordered coffee. [2] ________, she noticed a bag under her chair. She told the manager and he said, 'Thank you'. He asked Jan for her name, address and telephone number. [3] ________, she did some more shopping and went home. The [4] ________ day, a woman came to her house. 'You found my bag. Thanks so much! Here are two tickets for my next concert.' It was K T Trickster, the pop singer! Two weeks [5] ________, Jan and Martha had an amazing time at the concert.

B **USING SEQUENCING WORDS** Read the story again and complete it with *after*, *later*, *next* or *then*.

WRITING PRACTICE

A **PLAN** You are going to write about a past event. Read the beginning of a story. Write notes about what happened next.

Last Saturday, it was nice and sunny, so I went for a walk on the beach. After half an hour, I decided to go back home. Then I saw …

B **WRITE** Write your paragraph about a past event. Use your notes from Exercise A to help you. Remember to use sequencing words to order the events.

VOCABULARY
Recreational activities

A Complete *Life in your 20s – is the party over?* with the verbs in the box.

get go (x2) listen spend watch

Life in your 20s
– is the party over?

For a lot of people between the ages of 20 and 30, it is a time to meet friends and [1] ____________ to sporting events, cafés or restaurants. But more and more people in their 20s are saying that they mostly stay in, and the problem is usually money.

Sam, 27, told us, 'Even the burger place is a little expensive. We like to [2] ____________ some takeout food and meet at someone's house. We sometimes [3] ____________ to music, but we usually just talk'.

Chantelle, 22, said, 'I [4] ____________ movies or videos online, but it's a little boring when you do it alone, so my friends come to my apartment. I don't [5] ____________ to concerts anymore because I don't enjoy them – and the tickets are so expensive.'

Money isn't the only reason. A lot of young people told us that they want to [6] ____________ more time with their friends and family – and staying in is the best way to do this.

B Match the beginnings of the sentences (1–6) to the endings (a–f).

1 On Friday nights, we get ___
2 I always try to spend ___
3 Sometimes, I go to the ___
4 When I'm alone, I listen ___
5 Sharon doesn't watch ___
6 I like good food, so once a month, I go to ___

a a restaurant to eat.
b a lot of TV.
c some takeout food and eat it at my apartment.
d some time with my parents on the weekends.
e to music.
f park near my house for a walk.

C Match the words in the box to the correct verbs. Write them in the correct circles.

a concert a museum ~~a restaurant~~ a soccer game a video online family friends soccer on TV takeout food the park TV

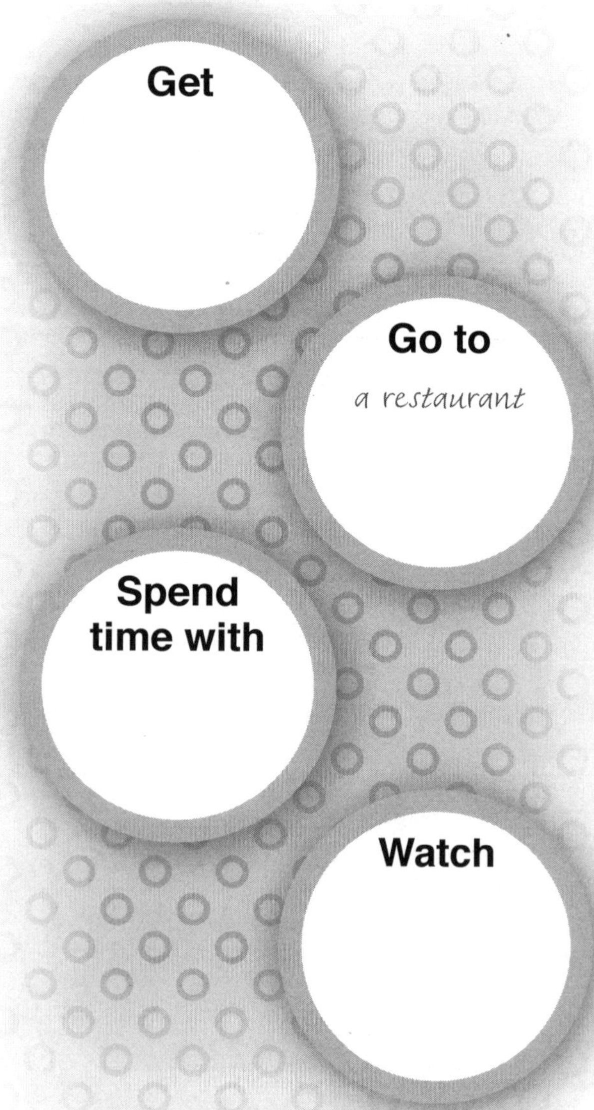

11.1 Having fun

In or out?

GRAMMAR
like/love/hate/enjoy + verb + *-ing*

A Choose the correct options (a, b or c) to complete the sentences.

1 Dina ___ online.
  a doesn't like chatting
  b isn't liking chatting
  c doesn't like chat

2 ___ out or staying in?
  a Do you like go
  b You like going
  c Do you like going

3 Eric ___ in expensive restaurants.
  a is enjoying eat
  b enjoys eating
  c enjoys eat

4 I ___ alone!
  a love being
  b loving being
  c love be

5 Johnny ___ to museums.
  a is hating going
  b hates going
  c hates go

6 ___ soccer with you?
  a Does your friend enjoy watch
  b Your friend he enjoys watching
  c Does your friend enjoy watching

B Reorder the words to make sentences.

1 tennis / playing / enjoy / We
______________________.

2 to / enjoy / you / theater / going / the / Do
______________________?

3 TV / watching / like / don't / I
______________________.

4 in / I / on the weekend / staying / hate
______________________.

5 like / he / alone / time / spending / Does
______________________?

6 going / concerts / don't / enjoy / They / to
______________________.

PRONUNCIATION
Verb + *-ing* /ŋ/

A 11.1 Listen to someone talking about their likes and dislikes. Complete the text with the missing words.

I like going out in the evening. I go into town and meet my friends. We enjoy [1] ______ at a café or [2] ______ out for a meal in a restaurant. Sometimes we watch a movie together, but the problem is we like [3] ______! At home, the thing I like doing most is [4] ______ to music. I enjoy being alone sometimes, but I love [5] ______ my friends when I can!

B 11.2 Listen and circle the word you hear.

1 ran / rang
2 sin / sing
3 sun / sung
4 kin / king

GRAMMAR
Object pronouns

A Choose the correct options to complete the sentences.

1 My wife likes online videos, but I don't watch ***them* / *they*** very often.
2 When my parents need something, they call ***I* / *me***.
3 She's a great singer – do you know ***she* / *her***?
4 Did you like that movie? I didn't understand ***it* / *me***.
5 We love our neighbor because she always helps ***us* / *we*** with the children.
6 Two of my son's teachers wanted to see me, so I went to see ***they* / *them***.
7 **A:** Did your parents give ***your* / *you*** that car?
B: No, I bought it.
8 **A:** What do you think of Ed Sheeran?
B: I like ***he* / *him***. I think his songs are great.

B There is one incorrect object pronoun in each sentence. Find and correct the mistakes.

1 He's a great soccer player and I love watching he play.
______
2 Jane likes concerts, but I don't like going to they.
______
3 She's a great jazz musician and I like she a lot.
______
4 I watched a baseball game, but I didn't understand him.
______
5 Our son usually gives we pictures he draws at school.
______
6 Yes, I know Steve – I sometimes play tennis with he.
______
7 I don't like the way that big dog is looking at I!
______
8 We love the theater – would you like to come with we sometime?
______

C Complete the sentences with an object pronoun.

1 He loves his guitar. He plays ______ every day.
2 My husband bought ______ a beautiful necklace for my last birthday.
3 Our parents gave ______ some money to buy a car.
4 He bought some new shoes last month, but he never wears ______.
5 Her boyfriend buys her flowers every week, but she never buys anything for ______.
6 I saw ______ yesterday but she didn't see me.
7 Do you have my book? I think I gave it to ______ last week.
8 The phone is ringing! Please answer ______.

VOCABULARY
Entertainment

A In each group of words, circle the odd one out, and say why it does not fit.

1	pop	comedy	rock	classical
2	basketball	baseball	stadium	tennis
3	movie star	musician	pop star	concert
4	movie theater	actor	player	singer
5	sci-fi	horror	classical	comedy
6	concert	game	actor	movie theater

1 ______________________

2 ______________________

3 ______________________

4 ______________________

5 ______________________

6 ______________________

B Complete the text with the correct form of circled words from Exercise A.

I don't really like home entertainment so I go out – a lot! I usually go to [1] ____________ because I'm a big music fan. I like pop and rock bands, but sometimes I listen to [2] ____________ music, too – I love listening to violins and cellos.

I sometimes go to sporting events, too. Baseball is my favorite. I like being with all the other fans in the [3] ____________ – it's really exciting.

And once a month, I go to the [4] ____________ to see a movie. I like watching something funny, so I always choose a [5] ____________. I like seeing good [6] ____________ in action movies, too.

PRONUNCIATION
Vowel sounds: /ʊ/ and /u:/

A 11.3 Listen and choose the correct sound for the underlined words.

1 Was it a good book? /ʊ/ /u:/

2 We soon found the school. /ʊ/ /u:/

3 Is it true that sugar is bad for you? /ʊ/ /u:/

4 It was June, and we took some food to the beach. /ʊ/ /u:/

5 My foot hurts – I think there's something in my shoe. /ʊ/ /u:/

6 200 years ago, they didn't use many books in schools. /ʊ/ /u:/

B Put the words into the correct place in the table.

book food school shoe took true two you

/ʊ/	/u:/

C Underline the words that have an /ʊ/ or /u:/. Then add them to the table in Exercise B.

1 I played tennis last Tuesday.

2 Stop pushing me!

3 Look at the rainbow! It's amazing.

4 I bought a new T-shirt yesterday.

5 I really like listening to rock music.

6 I can't carry this glass – it's too full!

7 You should eat more fruit!

8 I can't run right now, I've hurt my foot.

READING

A PREPARE TO READ Look at the pictures in *Time well spent*. Answer the questions.

1 How often do you go to a café?
2 What do you usually eat and drink there?
3 What do you like doing at a café?
4 How long do you usually spend in a café?

B READ FOR GIST Read the article. Did the writer enjoy their visit to the café? Why/Why not?

C READ FOR DETAIL Read the article again. Choose the correct options to complete the sentences.

1 The writer normally spends time *alone* / *with friends* in cafés on Sunday mornings.
2 The writer *likes* / *doesn't like* going to new cafés.
3 The food and drink at The Clock Café are *expensive* / *free*.
4 Customers can bring their own *food* / *clocks*.
5 You *can* / *can't* use wi-fi at the café.
6 *One* / *Both* of the piano players *was* / *were* good.

D REFLECT Think about the answers to these questions.

1 Do you think The Clock Café is a good idea? Why/Why not?
2 Would you like to go there?

LISTENING

11.4 **A LISTEN FOR GIST** Listen to the first part of a conversation and answer the question.

Why are the people having a meeting today?

a to organize a concert
b to collect money for their club
c to arrange a trip to New York

11.5 **B LISTEN FOR OPINIONS** Listen to the whole conversation. Put a check (✓) if the speaker agrees with the idea. Put an ✗ if he/she disagrees.

Idea	Stevie	Ashley	Molly
concert			
sporting event			
movie night			

11.5 **C LISTEN FOR DETAIL** Listen again and complete the speakers' reasons with no more than two words.

1 Ashley thinks a concert is a good idea because they're in a ____________.
2 Molly doesn't have time to do a concert because she has a lot of ____________.
3 Ashley says they can't organize a sporting event now because it's ____________.
4 Stevie wants a movie night because ____________ watching movies.

D REFLECT Think about the answers to these questions.

1 Which idea do you think is the best?
2 What other ideas are there for collecting money for a club?

TIME *Well Spent*

I love going to cafés with my friends. And we love trying new and interesting places to get our coffee and cake.

We usually like to relax in a café on a Sunday morning, talking and reading the newspapers for hours. But some cafés hate it when customers stay for a long time without buying more food. It's bad for their business. But then I heard about a new café called The Clock Café, where you only pay for the time you spend there, not what you eat or drink! Last Sunday, my friends and I went to try it.

You can have all the free snacks, tea and coffee you like, or you can bring and prepare your own food in the kitchen. (You have to wash your own dishes, though!) When you leave, you just pay for how long you were there – 6¢ for every minute or $3.60 per hour per person. That's the same price as for a piece of cake and a coffee in some places, so it is not expensive!

The café has its own special coffee and many different kinds of tea and cakes. It's also a good place to study or work because there's free wi-fi … but it's not always quiet. There's a piano there and somebody started playing when we were there. He wasn't very good, but then somebody else wanted to play and she was amazing!

I think it's a great place – the coffee and cakes are delicious, and it's a good place to relax and read or spend time with friends. The piano is an interesting idea – I guess it depends on who's playing!

FUNCTIONAL LANGUAGE

Making and responding to suggestions

1.6 **A Listen and choose the correct options to complete the sentences.**

1. They're talking about their plans for *today / tomorrow*.
2. They decide *not to go / to go* swimming.
3. Alex wants to *relax / go shopping*.

1.6 **B Listen again and answer the questions.**

1. When does Alex have free time?
2. What does George suggest they do?
3. Why doesn't Alex want to go swimming in the ocean?
4. What does Alex suggest?
5. Do they agree to go to the classical music concert?
6. What do they agree to do?

1.6 **C Complete the conversation with the words in the box. Then listen and check your answers.**

busy don't free How let's meet perfect sure

George: Alex?
Alex: Yeah?
George: Are you [1] ________________ tomorrow?
Alex: I have things to do in the morning, but I'm [2] ________________ after lunch. Do you want to meet for coffee?
George: No, [3] ________________ do something different tomorrow.
Alex: Like what?
George: [4] ________________ about going swimming at the recreation center? Or going to the beach for a swim in the ocean?
Alex: In the ocean?! Oh no – it's too cold. No – I don't want to do anything outdoorsy. I just want to relax tomorrow.
George: OK. What do you suggest?
Alex: Why [5] ________________ we go to a classical music concert?
George: A concert is OK, but I'm not [6] ________________ about classical music – I'm not really a big fan. What about going to the park and listening to the jazz musicians there?
Alex: That sounds [7] ________________. Let's do that.
George: Great. So when and where exactly do you want to [8] ________________?
Alex: What about meeting outside our building at 3 pm?
George: Cool – see you there!

WRITING

A Read the personal profile. Then choose the correct options to complete the sentences.

1. Gerry *writes / takes pictures* for a *vacation / travel* magazine.
2. He lives *with his family / alone* in a(n) *apartment / house*.
3. He *has / doesn't have* a dog, but he *likes / doesn't like* them.
4. He *doesn't enjoy / enjoys* watching soccer on TV.

ABOUT ME: Gerry P.

I'm a photographer for a vacation magazine, so I travel to many different places around the world. It's an interesting job and I love it. People tell me my pictures are very good, so I hope to show them in a gallery soon. I don't have a family and I live alone in a small apartment in New York. I travel a lot, so I don't have any pets – but I like dogs. I'm a soccer fan and my team is New York City FC. Their stadium is close to my house, but I don't often go to soccer games. I don't like crowds, so I prefer to watch games on TV with my friends.

B USING *SO* Read the profile again. Read the sentences where the writer uses *so* and answer the questions.

1. Why does Gerry travel a lot? Because …
   a he takes photographs for a magazine about vacations.
   b he likes vacations.
   c he is interested in seeing different parts of the world.
2. Why does he want to show his pictures in a gallery? Because …
   a he thinks galleries are interesting.
   b people think his photographs are good.
   c his family thinks it is a good idea.
3. Why doesn't he have pets? Because …
   a he doesn't like animals.
   b he's not at home often.
   c he only has a small apartment.
4. Why does he watch soccer games on TV? Because …
   a his friends prefer watching them on TV.
   b it's a long way to his team's stadium.
   c he doesn't like crowds.

WRITING PRACTICE

A PLAN You are going to write a personal profile about a friend. Write notes about his/her work, family and hobbies.

B WRITE Use your notes from Exercise A to write the personal profile. Remember to use *so* to talk about results.

VOCABULARY
Travel

A Reorder the letters in bold to complete the text.

The Johnson family booked their vacation to Europe months ago. They also booked a [1]**taix** to come to the house and take them to the [2]**trapoir** to get to their [3]**napel**. They changed their money into [4]**esuor**. They put all their clothes in three suitcases and their [5]**sportpass** in a small [6]**gab** which Mr. Johnson put near the door. Then they went to bed.

But in the morning, the taxi didn't come, probably because there was a lot of [7]**factrif**. There were no buses, so they decided to go by [8]**nitra**. They started to go to the station on [9]**foto**, but they were very slow because their [10]**glaguge** was too big. But luckily, on the way, their friend saw them and gave them a ride in her car.

1 ______ 6 ______
2 ______ 7 ______
3 ______ 8 ______
4 ______ 9 ______
5 ______ 10 ______

B Complete the sentences with the words in the box.

bike credit luggage money ticket trolleys

1 How much does a bus ______ cost?
2 Some cities have ______, but not all.
3 I would like to pay by ______ card, please.
4 Thomas spent all his ______ on souvenirs.
5 Can you get all your ______ in the car?
6 Chris goes to work by ______ because it's healthy.

C Complete the conversation with the words in the box.

airport credit card luggage money passport taxi tickets traffic

Phil: Hey! I'm excited about tomorrow! Do you want to book a [1] ______ to go to the [2] ______?

Hollie: Yes! I have a lot of [3] ______, so I don't want to take the train.

Phil: OK, great. I'll book it now. There's normally a lot of [4] ______ in the mornings, so I will book it for 6 am. Is that OK?

Hollie: Yes. I'm going to check in online now and print the [5] ______.

Hollie: Oh dear. I can't. You booked the tickets, so I need the [6] ______ you used to book!

Phil: Don't worry. I can do it when I get home.

Hollie: Thanks! I'm going to the bank to get some [7] ______. Then I'm going to pack my suitcase!

Phil: OK. See you in the morning. Don't forget your [8] ______!

PRONUNCIATION
Consonant clusters

A Listen and complete the sentences with the missing words. 12.1

1 I took the trolley to the airport and then got on my ______.
2 I never fly first ______.
3 The train is waiting at the ______.
4 Is your car ______ or black?
5 Would you like a soft drink or some ______ tea?
6 We have broccoli, grapes, ______ and bread.

B Listen to the sentences from Exercise A again. Then listen and repeat. 12.1

GRAMMAR
Countable and uncountable nouns

A **In each pair of sentences (1–10), choose the correct option.**

1 **a** Your money is in my bag.
b Your moneys are in my bag.

2 **a** She gave me a lot of information about things to do in Edinburgh.
b She gave me an information about things to do in Edinburgh.

3 **a** We waited for three hour for the next train.
b We waited for three hours for the next train.

4 **a** What musics do you like?
b What music do you like?

5 **a** I don't have any cashes with me.
b I don't have any cash with me.

6 **a** I was late because of all the traffic on the road.
b I was late because of all the traffics on the road.

7 **a** We had some food on the plane.
b We had a food on the plane.

8 **a** Did you bring the luggage?
b Did you bring the luggages?

9 **a** I have two ticket.
b I have two tickets.

10 **a** I need to do my homework on the train.
b I need to do my homeworks on the train.

B **Complete the sentences with the words in parentheses. Make one of the words plural.**

1 I don't have any ________ with me, but I have two ________. (*credit card / money*)

2 We have some ________ of juice, or would you like some ________ to drink? (*water / bottle*)

3 I brought my English ________ on vacation, but it's just a few ________. (*homework / exercise*)

4 She had some ________ at home, so she doesn't want these ________! (*sandwich / food*)

5 **A:** Was there a lot of ________?
B: No, just a few ________. (*traffic / car*)

6 **A:** Do you have a lot of ________?
B: No, only two ________. (*bag / luggage*)

7 **A:** Do you want to listen to some ________ in the car or should we sing a couple of ________? (*song / music*)

8 **A:** I need to get some ________.
B: Don't worry, I have ten ________! (*cash / credit card*)

9 **A:** Hurry up – we're going to be late! The plane leaves in two ________.
B: It's OK. We have lots of ________. (*time / hour*)

10 **A:** There isn't any ________ in the fridge.
B: I know. I bought you some ________ for lunch. (*sandwich / food*)

VOCABULARY
Types of vacations

A Unscramble the letters to make words connected to vacations.

1 acamer ____________
2 incapmg ____________
3 ssgunslsae ____________
4 ikss ____________
5 tohel ____________
6 entt ____________
7 aechb ____________
8 leacht ____________
9 iisngk olesggg ____________
10 gheetssigin ____________
11 giskni ____________
12 korseln ____________

B Put the words from Exercise A in the correct category. You can use two words twice.

Types of vacations	Places to stay	Things you need by the ocean	Things you need in the mountains
____________	____________	____________	____________
____________	____________	____________	____________
____________	____________	____________	____________
____________			____________

C Choose the correct options to complete the text.

About | Profile | Blog | Contact

BLOG

Vacations
THEN AND NOW

When Pausanias wrote a [1]***guidebook* / *stove* / *chalet*** about Greece, the people he wrote it for were very different from the [2]***sunglasses* / *tourists* / *goggles*** who go there today. That's because it was nearly 2,000 years ago, and when people went [3]***to* / *for* / *on*** vacation in those days, it was for months or years – not for two weeks. Yes, all those years ago, people went sightseeing [4]***on* / *for* / *around*** different places.

Today, people want to go by plane to somewhere hot, to see the ocean [5]***in* / *from* / *over*** their hotel window or to go skiing [6]***in* / *at* / *with*** the mountains and take photos [7]***to* / *for* / *with*** their cameras. But there are a lot of people who enjoy camping [8]***to* / *at* / *with*** friends, too.

All they need is a tent and a [9]***stove* / *snorkel* / *goggles*** to cook on. It's not a very comfortable vacation, but it's a great way to see and enjoy the countryside.

PRONUNCIATION
/ɪ/, /iː/ and /aɪ/

A Complete the sentences with the words in the box that have the same sound as the underlined letters.

beach like ski time win winner

1 I want to read on the ________ for a week.
2 Did you ________ the competition?
3 Do you ________ my guidebook?
4 This ________, we didn't win a prize.
5 We can ________ or go sightseeing.
6 … and the ________ is … Tim Smith!

2.2 **B Listen and check your answers to Exercise A.**

2.3 **C Listen and choose the correct sound for the words.**

1 listen /ɪ/ /iː/ /aɪ/
2 people /ɪ/ /iː/ /aɪ/
3 time /ɪ/ /iː/ /aɪ/
4 please /ɪ/ /iː/ /aɪ/
5 white /ɪ/ /iː/ /aɪ/
6 dinner /ɪ/ /iː/ /aɪ/

GRAMMAR
Present progressive

A Find and correct the mistakes with the present progressive.

1 Where are you go on vacation this year?
____
2 I'm be driving to Boston in the morning.
____
3 Judith's meet Amanda at the train station.
____
4 I go on a sightseeing vacation next month – I'm very excited.
____
5 We're leave at five in the morning.
____
6 The manager doesn't working next week.
____
7 Are you take the train to Fresno?
____
8 Does your sister going on vacation with you?
____

B Are sentences 1–8 about now (N) or the future (F)?

1 The taxi's coming. Are you sure you're ready? ___
2 Are you taking your camera when you go on vacation? ___
3 We're not staying in a hotel this week – we're camping. ___
4 They're leaving next Wednesday. ___
5 She isn't going on vacation in the summer. ___
6 Where are they staying at the moment? ___
7 Why are you looking at the map? I know where we are. ___
8 His plane is arriving in an hour. ___

C Complete the sentences and questions with the present progressive form of the verbs in parentheses.

1 I'm not here next week. ________ my sister in Los Angeles. (*visit*)
2 He can't come to the party. ________ soccer on Friday. (*play*)
3 What ________ next Saturday? Do you want to go to the movies? (*do*)
4 Helen ________ at 8 pm on Friday. Let's pick her up at the station. (*arrive*)
5 ________ tomorrow, they can get up late! (*not work*)
6 I'm on my way home. Are you there or ________ tonight? (*go out*)

What's your vacation style?

We asked readers to tell us about their idea of a perfect vacation. Jade and Paul have two very different vacation styles.

I don't enjoy sightseeing or going to museums and galleries, so I find cities fairly boring. There are always lots of tourists and traffic. For me, camping vacations are the best type of vacation. Last summer, I traveled around California in an old van. I took a tent with me, too. In rainy weather, I slept in the van, and in hot sunny weather, I camped on the beach. In the mornings, I usually walked to a local town to buy food. I didn't have a lot of money, but that was OK because I didn't need to buy many expensive things. In the afternoons, I swam in the ocean and looked at the fish. Then, in the evenings, I cooked food on a stove and read my book or listened to music. I was so relaxed! Next year, I'm driving around Arizona in my van and some friends are coming with me.

My favorite type of vacation is in a city. I enjoy visiting museums and art galleries or interesting buildings. I love the feeling of being with tourists from all over the world. Last year, I went to Rome. I rented a car at the airport and drove to my hotel. I had a lot of luggage, so I didn't want to go by bus. I stayed in an expensive hotel in the city center. My room was fantastic – I could see the Colosseum from my window! During the day, I visited all the important sights and I had dinner at a different restaurant every evening. On my last day, I went shopping and bought a new camera and some sunglasses. I didn't bring cash but paid for everything with my credit card. Next year, I'm going to Australia. I want to lie on the beach and visit Sydney and Melbourne.

READING

A PREDICT Look at the pictures in *What's your vacation style?* What two types of vacations do you think the people like?

B READ FOR GIST Read the article. Which person, Jade or Paul, likes going on expensive vacations?

C READ FOR DETAIL Read the text again and complete the table with words and phrases in the box. There are three words or phrases you do not need.

a chalet a hotel a tent or van Arizona Australia
California Cambodia camping museums and galleries
Rome, Italy sightseeing skiing swimming

Vacation style	Paul	Jade
Favorite type of vacation		
He/She stays in …		
He/She likes …		
Last year's destination		
Next year's destination		

D REFLECT Think about the answers to these questions.

1 Which type of vacation do you prefer? Why?
2 Would you prefer to visit Arizona or Australia? Why?

LISTENING

A PREPARE TO LISTEN Look at the list of things. Write *W* for winter vacation, *S* for summer vacation or *B* for both.

1 camera	___	5 goggles	___
2 snorkel	___	6 passport	___
3 sunglasses	___	7 coat	___
4 skis	___		

12.4 **B LISTEN FOR GIST** Listen to a conversation about vacation plans and answer the questions with two words.

1 Are the two friends going to a hot or a cold place?
2 How are they traveling?

12.4 **C LISTEN FOR DETAIL** Listen again and choose the correct options to complete the sentences.

1 Rudi *is* / *isn't* ready for the vacation.
2 Rudi must take lots of *T-shirts* / *swimming things*.
3 The friends *are not* / *are* planning to eat in expensive restaurants.
4 Claudia can wear her dresses *in the daytime and in the evening* / *only in the evening*.
5 Rudi is taking *a coat* / *a jacket*.
6 Rudi must buy sunglasses and *a hat* / *a snorkel*.
7 *Claudia* / *Rudi* has the tickets.
8 Rudi *forgot* / *didn't forget* to buy a guidebook.

D REFLECT Think about the answers to these questions.

1 Do you spend a little or a long time getting ready for your vacations?
2 Do you buy new things before you go on vacation?

FUNCTIONAL LANGUAGE
Asking for and giving opinions

A Complete the sentences with the words in the box.

about busy cool idea really so think

a I don't think ______.
b That's a really ______ place.
c They're always ______ with long lines.
d How ______ a weekend away somewhere?
e It's ______ cold there.
f Sounds like a good ______.
g I ______ it's too expensive there.

B Complete the conversation with the missing sentences (a–g) from Exercise A.

Will: What are you two talking about?
Naomi: We want to do something together before Olivia goes to Madrid.
Will: 1___
Olivia: But we can't decide what to do.
Naomi: I know! 2___
Olivia: Perfect! But where?
Naomi: What about Italy? Florence is beautiful and has lots of museums and galleries.
Olivia: 3___ I went there two years ago. Also, I'm not sure I like museums and galleries. 4___
Naomi: That's true. OK, then. What about Reykjavík?
Olivia: No way! 5___ It's called Iceland for a reason.
Will: What about Paris?
Naomi: 6___ A coffee costs $6! What do you think, Olivia?
Olivia: I agree. What about Berlin? 7___
Naomi: That's a great idea. Let's go there!

2.5 **C** Listen to the conversation and check your answers to Exercises A and B.

WRITING

A Read Melissa's postcard. Where is she?

B **EDITING YOUR WRITING** Find and correct three mistakes with spelling, grammar and punctuation in each sentence.

a I got hear three days ago and Im going home on saturday.
b One week aren't long and I cant wait to come back again next yeer.
c Its hot and suny, so I go to the beech every day and swim.
d There are lots of musiums in athens – I am going to the Archeological Museum yesterday.

C Now complete the postcard with the missing sentences (a–d) from Exercise B.

Hi Gabriella,

I'm on vacation in Greece. 1___ I'm having a really great time here.

2___ The sea is nice and cool, not really cold like in New England. I have a new hat for the sun and a snorkel so I can see the fish when I'm swimming.

But I don't just go to the beach. 3___ It was really interesting to learn about the history of the area. I'm also doing a lot of sightseeing. Tomorrow, I'm going to the famous Acropolis.

There are lots of things to see and do. 4___

See you soon.

Melissa

D Read the completed postcard and answer the questions.

1 Where does Melissa go every day?
2 What new things has she gotten?
3 Did she enjoy visiting the Archaeological Museum?
4 Does she want to visit Greece again?

WRITING PRACTICE

A **PLAN** You are going to write a postcard to a friend. Think about your last vacation or imagine a dream vacation. Write notes on things to see, things to do, the weather, etc.

B **WRITE** Use your notes and ideas from Exercise A to write a postcard to a friend. Remember to check your spelling, grammar and punctuation when you finish.

Irregular Verbs

Base form	Simple past	Past participle
be	was/were	been
become	became	become
begin	began	begun
break	broke	broken
bring	brought	brought
build	built	built
buy	bought	bought
can	could	been able to
catch	caught	caught
choose	chose	chosen
come	came	come
cost	cost	cost
cut	cut	cut
drink	drank	drunk
eat	ate	eaten
fall	fell	fallen
feel	felt	felt
find	found	found
forget	forgot	forgotten
get	got	got
give	gave	given
go	went	gone/been
grow	grew	grown
have	had	had
hear	heard	heard
hit	hit	hit
hold	held	held
hurt	hurt	hurt
keep	kept	kept
know	knew	known
leave	left	left
lend	lent	lent
let	let	let

Base form	Simple past	Past participle
lose	lost	lost
make	made	made
mean	meant	meant
meet	met	met
must	had to	had to
pay	paid	paid
put	put	put
read	read	read
ride	rode	ridden
run	ran	run
say	said	said
see	saw	seen
sell	sold	sold
send	sent	sent
set	set	set
shut	shut	shut
sing	sang	sung
sit	sat	sat
sleep	slept	slept
speak	spoke	spoken
spell	spelled	spelled
spend	spent	spent
stand	stood	stood
steal	stole	stolen
take	took	taken
teach	taught	taught
tell	told	told
think	thought	thought
throw	threw	thrown
understand	understood	understood
wear	wore	worn
win	won	won
write	wrote	written

PHONETIC SYMBOLS														
Single vowels			Diphthongs			Consonants								
/ɪ/	f**i**sh	/fɪʃ/	/uw/	n**ews**	/nuw/	/p/	**p**en	/pen/	/s/	**s**nake	/sneɪk/
/iː/	b**ea**n	/biːn/	/eɪ/	f**a**ce	/feɪs/	/b/	**b**ag	/bæg/	/z/	**z**oo	/zuː/
/ʊ/	f**oo**t	/fʊt/	/ɔɪ/	b**oy**	/bɔɪ/	/t/	**t**ea	/tiː/	/ʃ/	**sh**op	/ʃɒp/
/uː/	sh**oe**	/ʃuː/	/oʊ/	n**o**se	/noʊz/	/d/	**d**og	/dɒg/	/ʒ/	televi**si**on	/'telɪvɪʒən/
/e/	**e**gg	/eg/	/ju/	**u**se	/juz/	/ʧ/	**ch**ip	/ʧɪp/	/m/	**m**ap	/mæp/
/ə/	moth**er**	/'mʌðər/	/aɪ/	**eye**	/aɪ/	/ʤ/	**j**azz	/ʤæz/	/n/	**n**ame	/neɪm/
/ɜː/	w**or**d	/wɜːrd/	/aʊ/	m**ou**th	/maʊθ/	/k/	**c**ake	/keɪk/	/ŋ/	ri**ng**	/rɪŋ/
/ɔː/	t**al**k	/tɔːk/				/g/	**g**irl	/gɜːrl/	/h/	**h**ouse	/haʊs/
/æ/	b**a**ck	/bæk/				/f/	**f**ilm	/fɪlm/	/l/	**l**eg	/leg/
/ʌ/	b**u**s	/bʌs/				/v/	**v**erb	/vɜːrb/	/r/	**r**oad	/roʊd/
/ɑː/	**ar**m	/ɑːrm/				/θ/	**th**ing	/θɪŋ/	/w/	**w**ant	/wɒnt/
/ɒ/	t**o**p	/tɒp/				/ð/	**th**ese	/ðiːz/	/j/	**y**es	/jes/

UNIT 7

Lesson 7.3, Listening, Exercise B
.4 **M = Manu R = Rachel**

M: What are you doing, Rachel?

R: Oh, hi, Manu. I'm writing a letter for my French class.

M: Oh, are you learning French now?

R: Yes, I am. I can speak a lot of languages – English, of course, and some Spanish, and now I'm learning French.

M: Three languages? That's great!

R: What about you? Just English? You can come to my French class if you want or I can teach you some words and phrases.

M: Well, … um … My mother's from Morocco and she speaks perfect French. I go there every summer to visit my grandparents. They only speak Arabic and we always speak it when we're together, so you see – I speak French and Arabic.

R: Oh!

M: Then there's my father.

R: Does he speak French and Arabic, too?

M: No, he doesn't speak Arabic, but he speaks English and French because he's from Canada – from Montreal. So at home we usually speak French. And then it's English here at the university of course.

R: Anything else?

M: Well, yes. My parents live in Mexico City now. My dad's an engineer there.

R: Oh. What language do they speak in Mexico?

M: Spanish – both my parents speak very good Spanish.

R: Oh, but you don't speak Spanish?

M: Well, yes. My Spanish is very good. I don't go there very often because it's a long way and the airfare is expensive, but it's an easy language to learn.

R: Easy? I can only say 'Hello' and 'How are you?' It's really difficult!

M: Don't worry – I can teach you if you want. Now – do you want me to help you with your French homework?

R: Yes, please!

UNIT 8

Lesson 8.3, Listening, Exercise B
8.3 **M = Male F = Female**

M: What are you doing?

F: I'm reading a magazine. Hey, look! There's a competition.

M: Find seven differences between the two pictures. Cool!

F: Let's do it.

M: OK … let me see. Both the pictures are in a park.

F: Yes, that's right. In Picture 1, there's a woman sitting on a bench.

M: Yes, she's reading a newspaper.

F: So … that's the same. Oh – no! Look – in Picture 2, she's reading a book.

M: So that's the first difference. Good job! There are two children playing soccer … two boys … but in Picture 2, there's a girl and a boy.

F: Oh, yes. There's a dog playing with them, too. A big black dog.

M: In the first picture, yes. In the second picture, the dog's black and white.

F: Yes, and it's small – a small black and white dog. OK. What about the two young women?

M: Hmm … in Picture 1, they're playing chess.

F: I think they're the same. They're also playing chess in Picture 2. Oh, no! This woman has long dark hair, but in the first picture, she has short dark hair.

M: Yes, you're right. Hey, look. There's something else. In Picture 1, it's sunny and warm, but in Picture 2, there isn't any sunshine. I think it's cold.

F: That's true. It's summer in Picture 1. I think that's it.

M: No, it says 'seven differences', and we've only found five.

F: OK … oh … look at the woman running. Here, she's wearing black sneakers and in the other picture, she isn't wearing black sneakers; her sneakers are white!

M: Oh, yes. And … that's number six! And the last difference?

F: Let me see … oh, no!

M: What?

F: It's five fifty! I start work in ten minutes. I'm late!

M: Oh, OK. See you …

F: Sorry! Bye!

Lesson 8.4, Functional Language,
8.4 **Exercise A**
L = Lauren G = Grace A = Assistant

L: Hey, Grace. That store has what you want.

G: It does? OK, let's go there.

A: Good morning. Can I help you?

G: We're just looking, thanks.

L: Hold on, Grace. Actually, she's looking for a T-shirt.

A: Of course. We have a lot of them. What size would you like?

G: Small, please.

A: No problem. And what color would you like?

G: Do you have a red one?

A: Is this one OK?

G: Hmm. It's not bad. Lauren, what do you think?

L: I think it's horrible. Buy the blue one.

G: OK. How much is it?

A: $15.

G: Thanks, I'll take it.

UNIT 9

Lesson 9.3, Listening, Exercise B
9.4 **A = Announcer T = Tom**

A: Good evening and welcome to *Quick Quiz*! The competition where you have to answer as fast as you can on a special subject of your choice. Who's first on tonight's show?

Hello! Tell us your name.

T: Um … hi. I'm Tom Harris.

A: Let's hear it for Tom Harris, everybody!

Tom – are you ready?

T: Yes.

A: Your special subject is 20th-century writers and painters. First question: for $100. What nationality was Claude Monet? Was he a) Spanish, b) French or c) Belgian?

T: He was French.

A: That's right. Well done! Second question: for $200. When was the painter Pablo Picasso born? Was it a) 1875, b) 1894 or c) 1881?

T: Um … Let's see. I think 1875 is too early … and 1881 is too early, too. I think it's … oh dear … b) 1894.

A: Um, sorry, Tom! That is *not* the right answer. Pablo Picasso was born in 1881. So you get no money for that question. Let's try again with your third question – again for $200.

Joseph Conrad, the writer, was born Jozef Teodor Konrad Korzeniowski in northern Ukraine, but his books were in what language? Were they a) in Polish, b) in English or c) in French?

T: Well, his family was Polish and his name, too, of course … but I think … hmm … yes, I think his books were in English.

A: Yes, Tom! Perfect! $200 is yours! Next question: for $400. That's a lot of money, so be careful now. What was the name of the style of art which Andy Warhol used in his paintings? Was it a) pop art, b) selfie-art or c) world art?

T: OK. I know this. It's a) pop art.

A: Yes! Next question, and for $800, it's a difficult one! Which of these writers studied to be a doctor before becoming famous? Was it a) Michael Crichton, b) Margaret Atwood or c) Stephen King?

T: Oh, dear. I don't know the answer to this question. I guess … Michael Crichton – no – um, or Stephen King? … or …

A: I'm sorry, but your time is up. The correct answer to the last question was – Michael Crichton. Tom – you are leaving with $400. Well done!

T: Thank you!

Lesson 9.4, Functional Language, Exercise A
9.5
I = Izzie D = Dev

I: Do you know any good restaurants around here?

D: Yes, I do. What do you like? Indian food? Japanese? Italian?

I: My favorite is Mexican food.

D: Let me see … There are three Mexican restaurants in town – I'll show you on the map. Don't go to this one – I was there on Saturday night and the food was terrible, *and* it wasn't cheap.

I: OK.

D: Now this one isn't far, but I wouldn't go there, either. It's also too expensive.

I: OK. And the third one?

D: Yes! You should definitely go to that one. It's my favorite!

I: How do I get there?

D: Um. It's kind of far away. Why don't you take a taxi?

I: Are there any other good, cheap restaurants nearby?

UNIT 10

Lesson 10.3, Listening, Exercise B
10.3
J = Jason P = Polly

J: We had a fantastic day at the V and A last week.

P: The V and A?

J: Yes, the Victoria and Albert Museum. It's in London.

P: Oh, OK.

J: They built it when Victoria was Queen of England. That's why it has her name.

P: So when was that?

J: Well, she was born in 1837 and died in 1901.

P: No, I mean, when did they build the museum?

J: Oh, I see. In 1852. It's a museum of art and design – it has more than 2.2 million objects in it.

P: Wow! So what was your favorite object in the museum?

J: Hmm – that's a difficult question because there were a lot of interesting things there. I really liked the metal collection. There were hundreds of different objects. I really liked a gold model of a boat which a very rich man kept salt in! I also saw amazing objects from ancient Egypt – there was a beautiful necklace shaped like a snake. It was more than a thousand years old!

P: What else did you see?

J: The fashion collection was amazing.

P: Do you like fashion?

J: No, not really, but this was different. There were pictures, notebooks and clothes from hundreds of years ago, as well as modern clothes.

P: Did you see the dress that Princess Diana wore when she got married?

J: No, I didn't. I think that's in a different museum – not the V and A.

P: I'd like to see that.

J: The best object was a wooden tiger.

P: A tiger?

J: Yes, they're my favorite animals; that's the reason I liked it. It's called 'Tipu's Tiger' and it was from India – from the 18th century. It's made of wood and … well … it's a type of toy really, but not for children – maybe that's why people like it. It's one of the most popular objects in the museum. Actually, there are so many things that I didn't have time to see everything. I'd like to go again.

P: Maybe I can come with you next time.

J: Good idea!

Lesson 10.4, Functional Language, Exercise C
10.4
S = Seb L = Leila M = Mike C = Chris

S: Hi, Leila. How was your weekend?

L: Hi, Seb. Not good. I went shopping and bought some new headphones, and then guess what? I left them on the bus! In the evening, I went out for a pizza with my parents, but it was terrible!

S: That sounds awful. Oh look, here come Mike and Chris.

M: Hi guys. What are you talking about?

S: What we did over the weekend. Leila says she had a terrible weekend.

M: Oh. What a shame. I went to New York City with my brother.

L: Really? Wow!

C: Yes, that sounds amazing.

M: Yes, it was. What did you do Chris?

C: I just stayed at home and watched soccer with some friends.

L: That's nice. Was it a good game?

C: Yes, I really enjoyed it. My team won.

S: I watched the game, too. It was a great game.

UNIT 11

Lesson 11.3, Listening, Exercise B
11.5
S = Stevie A = Ashley M = Molly

S: Good morning. Hi, Molly. Hi, Ashley.

A & M: Hi, Stevie.

S: Thanks for coming. Now – you know that we need to collect money for the music club. We want to buy new books and instruments for the weekend workshops, and we want to go on a trip to New York to the Musical Museum. What can we do to collect some money? Any ideas? Ashley?

A: Well, we *are* a *music* club … Why don't we organize a concert?

S: I think that's a great idea, Ashley. We can all sing a song or play our instruments. Molly, what do you think?

M: I'm not sure about that. I don't have time to practice any new songs because I have a lot of work right.

S: Well, OK. Do you have any other ideas, Molly?

M: Yes, I do. What about a sporting event? A soccer game? Or a race?

S: I'm sorry, but that sounds a bit … well, a bit boring. Ashley?

A: I think that's a terrible idea! We're a music club, not a sports club! And we can't have a sporting event because it's winter now, and the weather is cold and rainy. No, I don't think that's a good plan.

S: Do we have any other suggestions?

A: Um … I really love movies.

S: Yes, Ashley? And?

A: How about having a movie night?

S: Good idea. Everybody enjoys watching movies. Molly?

M: Yes, OK. That sounds interesting. Let's have a movie about a famous musician.

S: Yes, I think that's a great idea.

11.6 Lesson 11.4, Functional Language, Exercise A

G = George A = Alex

G: Alex?

A: Yeah?

G: Are you busy tomorrow?

A: I have things to do in the morning, but I'm free after lunch. Do you want to meet for coffee?

G: No, let's do something different tomorrow.

A: Like what?

G: How about going swimming at the recreation center? Or going to the beach for a swim in the ocean?

A: In the ocean?! Oh no – it's too cold. No – I don't want to do anything outdoorsy. I just want to relax tomorrow.

G: OK. What do you suggest?

A: Why don't we go to a classical music concert?

G: A concert is OK, but I'm not sure about classical music – I'm not really a big fan. What about going to the park and listening to the jazz musicians there?

A: That sounds perfect. Let's do that.

G: Great. So when and where exactly do you want to meet?

A: What about meeting outside our building at 3 pm?

G: Cool – see you there!

UNIT 12

12.4 Lesson 12.3, Listening, Exercise B

R = Rudi C = Claudia

R: Hi, Claudia. It's Rudi here.

C: Oh, hi, Rudi. Are you ready?

R: Um … no … not really. That's why I'm calling you. What clothes are you taking?

C: Well, it's really hot in Las Palmas, so take light clothes – lots of T-shirts, some shorts … and your swimming things, of course.

R: Great. What about the evenings?

C: Well, we're not going anywhere really expensive, are we? I'm taking two dresses for eating out in the evening, but of course I can wear them in the day, too, if I want. Why don't you take some nice pants for the evening? You can wear them with one of your T-shirts and they'll look fine.

R: OK. So no sweaters or coats, or anything?

C: No, it's not cold there, but take a jacket.

R: OK.

C: And a sun hat. Do you have sunglasses?

R: I have a hat, so that's OK. And I'm going shopping tomorrow to buy some sunglasses. Do I need anything else?

C: No, I don't think so. Oh … do you have a snorkel?

R: Yes, I do. What about you?

C: No, I don't. Can you buy me one tomorrow?

R: Sure. OK, bye then, Claudia …

C: Hold on!

R: What's the matter?

C: I have our tickets, but don't forget your passport.

R: No, don't worry. I have a small bag with my passport, my money and my credit cards. Oh, I almost forgot. I bought a guidebook yesterday, so you don't need to get one.

C: Oh, that was a good idea. We can read it on the plane. OK – see you on Saturday morning at the airport.

R: Great. I'm really excited! See you soon. Bye, Claudia.

C: Bye, Rudi!

12.5 Lesson 12.4, Functional Language, Exercise C

W = Will N = Naomi O = Olivia

W: What are you two talking about?

N: We want to do something together before Olivia goes to Madrid.

W: Sounds like a good idea.

O: But we can't decide what to do.

N: I know! How about a weekend away somewhere?

O: Perfect! But where?

N: What about Italy? Florence is beautiful and has lots of museums and galleries.

O: I don't think so. I went there two years ago. Also, I'm not sure I like museums and galleries. They're always busy with long lines.

N: That's true. OK, then. What about Reykjavík?

O: No way! It's really cold there. It's called Iceland for a reason.

W: What about Paris?

N: I think it's too expensive there. A coffee costs $6! What do you think, Olivia?

O: I agree. What about Berlin? That's a really cool place.

N: That's a great idea. Let's go there!

Answer key

7.1 What can you do?

GRAMMAR

A

1 Can you dive **2** can teach **3** can't do **4** can help
5 can do **6** Can you help **7** can't drive

B

1 can hold **2** I can't **3** can't speak **4** Can you
5 can't cook **6** can you do **7** can fly **8** we can

C

2 She can climb a tree but she can't climb a wall.
3 He can swim in a pool but he can't swim in the ocean.
4 They can play soccer but they can't play basketball.
5 You can drive a car but you can't drive a bus.
6 She can make an omelette but she can't make a cake.
7 I can speak Spanish but I can't speak Japanese.
8 She can swim very far but she can't swim underwater.

PRONUNCIATION

A

1 a **2** a **3** b **4** b **5** a **6** b

C

1 can **2** can't **3** can't **4** can't **5** can **6** can

VOCABULARY

A

Make: a cake; an omelette
Play: tennis; the guitar; the piano
Ride: a bicycle; a horse
Speak: Chinese; French; Spanish

B

1 ski **2** paint **3** speak **4** ride **5** dance **6** cook
7 make **8** sing

C

1 paint **2** sing **3** drive **4** plays **5** rides **6** speak
7 do **8** juggle

7.2 He's amazing

VOCABULARY

A

w	f	g	n	i	r	p	p	d	o	a	r	s	h	o	r	t	a	s	p
s	v	a	a	w	w	u	f	e	l	x	a	i	a	s	e	e	r	p	e
e	t	i	n	t	e	r	e	s	t	i	n	g	u	g	a	d	e	e	f
r	i	e	e	r	b	b	n	f	j	z	a	e	i	f	p	q	e	a	f
s	i	g	r	e	a	t	m	b	y	a	i	e	m	g	u	u	d	s	s
y	m	n	e	a	a	b	s	c	m	c	n	g	o	o	d	s	t	y	o
o	l	k	s	t	y	u	i	a	d	d	m	s	n	f	p	o	g	y	i
u	y	u	s	s	r	r	p	s	i	e	o	x	n	s	i	o	x	t	i
n	e	d	o	o	l	d	p	c	f	r	s	b	e	e	i	e	j	s	n
g	m	i	g	l	l	e	a	t	f	h	d	o	r	e	r	l	m	t	g
i	n	t	f	a	w	f	w	h	i	m	h	r	p	o	e	o	n	b	b
n	e	r	h	e	i	l	n	m	c	e	j	i	s	p	p	n	f	v	a
g	a	w	f	u	l	t	n	i	u	r	k	n	e	y	n	g	q	e	d
n	n	m	h	u	t	r	a	f	l	b	r	g	t	t	a	h	a	i	d
d	i	f	n	m	w	a	v	k	t	e	d	o	p	q	s	s	z	e	r

B
interesting boring
good bad
old young
difficult easy
long short

C
1 a 2 b 3 b 4 a 5 a 6 a

D
1 talented 2 young 3 amazing 4 terrible
5 interesting 6 boring

GRAMMAR

A
1 sister's friend 2 brothers' 3 Marcus's 4 parents'
5 Harry's 6 colleague's 7 manager's office 8 Danny's

B
1 son's 2 Dina's 3 She's 4 name's 5 parents'
6 daughters' 7 armchair's 8 Olly's, sisters'

C
1 possessive *'s* 2 possessive *'s* 3 has 4 is 5 possessive *s'*
6 possessive *s'* 7 is 8 possessive *'s* / possessive *s'*

PRONUNCIATION

A
1 /z/ 2 /s/ 3 /iz/ 4 /z/

7.3 Reading; Listening

READING

A
playing basketball; swimming

B
1 for young people 2 don't usually

C
1 one week 2 team 3 ride 4 can't 5 safe 6 every year

LISTENING

A
1 English and French 2 English 3 Spanish
4 French and Arabic

B
1 three 2 four

C
1 e 2 f 3 a 4 c 5 b 6 d

7.4 Functional Language; Write a competition entry

FUNCTIONAL LANGUAGE

A
1 Hello, is that Mark's Hair?
2 I'd like to make an appointment, please.
3 Do you have time today?
4 Is two o'clock OK?

B
1 b 2 a

C
1 can 2 I'd like 3 Yes, of course. 4 would you like
5 Do you have 6 fine 7 would you like 8 Is 11:30 OK

WRITING

A
1 She's 22. 2 She's from Egypt.
3 speak languages; play music; cook.

B
1 speak 2 play 3 drums 4 meals 5 food

C
I'm Leila and I'm from Egypt. My father is Egyptian and my mother is Italian. I can speak Arabic, Italian and English. I really love music. I can sing and play the guitar, violin and drums.
I like to cook as well. I can cook amazing meals from different parts of the world. My favorite food is Italian, but I like Spanish, Mexican, Lebanese and Chinese, too.

WRITING PRACTICE

B

Model answer

Name: Nat Barclay **Age:** 23

About you: My friend's name is Nat and she's from Kansas. She's very talented! She loves sports and she's really good at soccer. She can also swim, ski and do judo. She loves music and people say she's a good dancer. She can sing, too, but she can't play a musical instrument. She can also speak three languages – French, Italian and German.

8.1 What's he doing?

GRAMMAR

A
1 doing 2 living 3 getting 4 watching 5 sitting
6 having 7 talking 8 meeting 9 going 10 working
11 taking 12 leaving

B
2 They're playing tennis. They aren't playing soccer.
3 We're waiting at the station.
4 You aren't / You're not listening to me.
5 I'm taking a nap.
6 She's drinking coffee.

C
1 I am 2 he isn't 3 we are 4 they aren't / they're not
5 she is 6 I'm not 7 they are 8 it isn't

D
2 Who are you talking to?
3 Where are you waiting for Jim?
4 When is she meeting her friend?
5 Why are you going home?
6 What is he reading?

E

1 'm not working **2** 'm cooking **3** are shopping
4 're looking **5** 's doing **6** 's also listening **7** 's singing
8 's not / isn't raining

VOCABULARY

A

1 going **2** meeting **3** take **4** looking **5** having
6 watch **7** reading **8** talk

B

1 meet **2** looking **3** take **4** have **5** reading **6** watch
7 go **8** talk

PRONUNCIATION

A

1 watch **2** talking **3** take **4** play **5** washes **6** falling
7 call **8** staying **9** catch

B

/æ/ catch
/eɪ/ take; play; staying
/ɔː/ talking; falling; call
/ɑ/ watch; washes

8.2 The gray coat

VOCABULARY

A

1 cap **2** T-shirt **3** shorts **4** sneakers **5** hat **6** dress
7 shoes **8** socks

B

1 b **2** a **3** b **4** b **5** a **6** b **7** a **8** b **9** b **10** b

C

2 shorts **3** dress **4** skirt **5** shirt

PRONUNCIATION

A

1 c **2** b **3** d **4** a

C

eat > TV > meet > pizza > team

D

four > short > warm > fall > ball

GRAMMAR

A

1 new green **2** long blue **3** short gray **4** long yellow
5 new white **6** old gray **7** big blue **8** great old

B

1 ✗ **2** ✓ **3** ✗ **4** ✓ **5** ✗ **6** ✗ **7** ✗ **8** ✓

8.3 Reading; Listening

READING

A

1 Ken **2** Jo **3** friends

B

1 Shanghai **2** party **3** hotel **4** colleagues **5** Sunday

C

1 F **2** T **3** F **4** F **5** F **6** T

LISTENING

A

In Picture 1, there's a big black dog. In Picture 2, there's a small black and white dog.

B

1 There are seven differences.
2 No, they don't.
3 Because she is late.

C

Model answer

Differences: Picture 1 – woman reading a newspaper, Picture 2 – woman reading a book. Picture 1 – two boys playing soccer, Picture 2 – a boy and a girl playing soccer.
Picture 1 – big black dog, Picture 2 – small black and white dog. Picture 1 – woman with short dark hair, Picture 2 – woman with long dark hair. Picture 1 – sunshine, Picture 2 – no sunshine. Picture 1– woman with white sneakers, Picture 2 – woman with black sneakers.
Final difference the speakers do not find: Picture 1 – the man sitting on the bench is not looking at his phone, Picture 2 – he's looking at his phone.

8.4 Functional Language; Write a short message

FUNCTIONAL LANGUAGE

A

1 F **2** F **3** F **4** T **5** T

B

1 How much is it? **2** We have a lot of them.
3 What color would you like? **4** She's looking for a T-shirt.
5 Can I help you?

C

1 Can I help you **2** she's looking for a T-shirt
3 We have a lot of them **4** what color would you like
5 How much is it

WRITING

A

2 He's with Tessa and Gerry.
3 Tessa is waiting for Olly.
4 Jasmine is studying.

B

1 too **2** too **3** also **4** Also

WRITING PRACTICE

Model answer

Hi Jamie. What are you doing?

Hi Karen. I'm sitting in the sun. I'm also watching a video on my phone.

Who's with you?

Hi, it's Jamal. I'm here, too. We're all waiting for Maria before we ride our bikes to the lake. Do you want to come, too?

I'd love to, but I can't. I'm shopping with my sister right now. Maybe next time.

9.1 Famous faces

GRAMMAR

A

1 were **2** wasn't **3** was **4** weren't **5** Were **6** was **7** were **8** were

B

2 Was she a great artist?
3 Were her paintings popular at first?
4 Were they too modern?
5 Were they popular later?
6 Were her paintings pictures of herself?

VOCABULARY

A

1 thirtieth **2** nineteen **3** twentieth **4** twenty-first **5** first

B

1 sixteenth **2** nineteen ninety **3** twelfth
4 two thousand and two **5** nineteen oh/o nine
6 seventh; eighth **7** fifteen sixty-four

PRONUNCIATION

A

1 ✓
2 Was he a painter?
3 Where was she born?
4 ✓
5 ✓
6 What year was he born?
7 Was she OK in the lesson?
8 ✓

9.2 Voices from the past

VOCABULARY

A

1 study; design **2** receive; help **3** collect; paint
4 start; travel

B

			[1]r	e	[2]c	e	i	v	e
[3]s					o				
[4]t	r	a	v	e	l		[5]p		
u					l		a		
d				[6]d	e	s	i	g	n
y					c		n		
					t		t		
							s		

C

1 studied **2** traveled **3** started **4** received
5 designed **6** helped

GRAMMAR

A

add *-d*: completed; circled
add *-ed*: started; painted
cut the *-y*, add *-ied*: cried; tried

B

1 received **2** want **3** didn't look **4** studied
5 started **6** study **7** cried **8** designed

C

1 started **2** didn't watch **3** collected **4** traveled
5 didn't paint **6** didn't talk **7** wanted **8** discovered
9 didn't call **10** received

PRONUNCIATION

A

1 decided **2** designed **3** helped **4** collected
5 cried **6** wanted

B

1 /d/ **2** /t/ **3** /ɪd/ **4** /ɪd/ **5** /d/ **6** /t/

9.3 Reading; Listening

READING

A

education

B

a 3 **b** 1 **c** 2

C

1 Kakenya Ntaiya **2** Kenya **3** 1978
4 school for girls (in her village)

D

1 hero **2** worked **3** studied **4** only for girls **5** the future

LISTENING

A

3

B

$400

C

1 b **2** c **3** b **4** a **5** a

9.4 Functional Language; Write a short biography

FUNCTIONAL LANGUAGE

A

1 Mexican
2 three
3 food was terrible; not cheap (expensive)
4 too expensive
5 It's far away; doesn't want to pay for a taxi (too expensive)

B

1 know **2** Don't **3** wouldn't **4** should **5** Why don't you
6 Are there

WRITING

A

1 Germany **2** Bauhaus

C

a 6 **b** 2 **c** 5 **d** 4 **e** 1 **f** 3

WRITING PRACTICE

B

Model answer

Louis Armstrong was born in New Orleans in 1901. He was a jazz musician who played the trumpet and sang. He also acted in movies. He made jazz popular. One famous song of his that everybody knows is 'What a wonderful world'.

10.1 Precious finds

GRAMMAR

A

1 found
2 gave
3 wore
4 send
5 took
6 chose
7 have
8 sold; bought

B

2 I wore jeans and a T-shirt yesterday.
3 I made a lot of phone calls last week.
4 They didn't have breakfast at home this morning.
5 She wrote a lot of emails yesterday.
6 You didn't send many text messages yesterday.
7 He took a lot of photographs on vacation last summer.
8 You bought a lot of new shoes last week!
9 I didn't see you yesterday.
10 He gave her flowers last Saturday!

C

1 wore **2** chose **3** made **4** have **5** bought **6** sell

VOCABULARY

A

In: 2002; 1986; the 1990s; the past
Ago: 20 years; a couple of minutes; two weeks; 100 years
Last: year; week; Tuesday

B

1 I had dinner with my wife last Friday.
2 The manager left an hour ago.
3 The company started in 2018.
4 We didn't work last week.
5 Someone made this snake in the 15th century.
6 These people lived a long time ago.
7 I found this job last year.
8 60 years ago, life was very different.

C

1 I went there ~~before~~ two years **ago**.
2 We had a meeting ~~on~~ last Friday.
3 They found the coins ~~the~~ last year.
4 **In** the past, there were trains, but not many cars.
5 I spoke to Jim an hour **ago** ~~before~~.
6 We had no work **last** ~~the past~~ week.
7 You missed the class ~~the~~ last Tuesday.
8 We met five years **ago** ~~past~~.

PRONUNCIATION

A

1 a **2** a **3** a **4** b **5** b **6** a

10.2 Family treasures

VOCABULARY

A

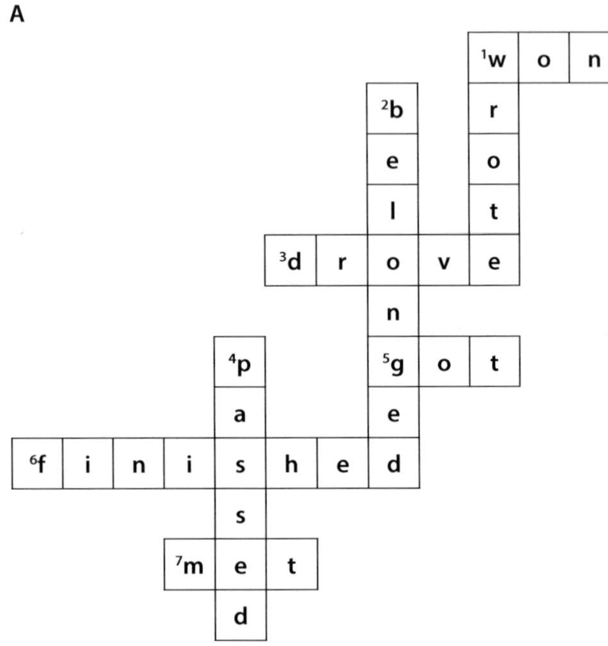

B

1 wrote **2** won **3** drove **4** belonged **5** passed **6** met **7** got **8** finished

GRAMMAR

A

1 When did they get married?
2 Did they get married in the spring?
3 Where did the wedding take place?
4 What time did it start?
5 How many people did they invite?
6 Why did they take this picture?
7 Who did they ask to take it?
8 Did they have an amazing day?

B

1 he didn't **2** she did **3** they didn't **4** it did **5** I didn't

C

2 How many emails did you send yesterday?
3 What did you finish last week?
4 When did your mother give you this ring?
5 Why did you leave the movie theater?
6 When did the train arrive?
7 Who did you call last night?
8 What did you buy yesterday?
9 Why did you go home?
10 How many paintings did they sell?

PRONUNCIATION

A

1 ride **2** sent **3** said **4** coat **5** built **6** spent

10.3 Reading; Listening

READING

A

the sundial

B

b

C

1 for thousands of years **2** big and small
3 time and distance **4** in towers **5** 1900s

LISTENING

A

museum

B

1 Yes, he did. **2** No, he didn't. **3** Yes, she does.

C

1 London **2** ~~in~~ 1852 **3** art and design **4** salt **5** necklace
6 didn't **7** his favorite animals **8** India

10.4 Functional Language; Write a paragraph about a past event

FUNCTIONAL LANGUAGE

A

1 d **2** c **3** e **4** g **5** b

B

1 terrible **2** sounds **3** talking **4** shame **5** amazing
6 watched **7** nice **8** enjoyed

WRITING

A

1 F **2** F **3** F **4** T **5** T

B

1 After **2** Then **3** Later **4** next **5** later

WRITING PRACTICE

B

Model answer

Last Saturday, it was nice and sunny, so I went for a walk on the beach. After half an hour, I decided to go back home. Then I saw something in the water. It was a necklace and it looked very expensive. I wasn't sure what to do with it. Then I decided to put an ad in the local newspaper. 'Found. One beautiful necklace. At Golden Beach.' The next day, a man came to my house and said it was his wife's necklace. He was very happy to get it back. Later that day, we all went to a nice restaurant to celebrate.

11.1 In or out?

VOCABULARY

A

1 go **2** get **3** listen **4** watch **5** go **6** spend

B

1 c **2** d **3** f **4** e **5** b **6** a

C

Get: takeout food
Go to: a concert; a soccer game; a museum; the park
Spend time with: family; friends
Watch: a video online; soccer on TV; TV

GRAMMAR

A

1 a **2** c **3** b **4** a **5** b **6** c

B

1 We enjoy playing tennis.
2 Do you enjoy going to the theater?
3 I don't like watching TV.
4 I hate staying in on the weekend.
5 Does he like spending time alone?
6 They don't enjoy going to concerts.

PRONUNCIATION

A

1 chatting **2** going **3** talking **4** listening **5** seeing

B

1 ran **2** sing **3** sung **4** king

11.2 Super fans

GRAMMAR

A

1 them **2** me **3** her **4** it **5** us **6** them
7 you **8** him

B

1 He's a great soccer player and I love watching **him** ~~he~~ play.
2 Jane likes concerts, but I don't like going to **them** ~~they~~.
3 She's a great jazz musician and I like **her** ~~she~~ a lot.
4 I watched a baseball game, but I didn't understand **it** ~~him~~.
5 Our son usually gives **us** ~~we~~ pictures he draws at school.
6 Yes, I know Steve – I sometimes play tennis with **him** ~~he~~.
7 I don't like the way that big dog is looking at **me** ~~I~~!
8 We love the theater – would you like to come with **us** ~~we~~ sometime?

C

1 it **2** me **3** us **4** them **5** him **6** her **7** you **8** it

VOCABULARY

A

1 comedy; the other words are types of music
2 stadium; the other words are sports
3 concert; the other words are people
4 movie theater; the other words are people
5 classical; the other words are types of movies
6 actor; the other words are things

B
1 concerts **2** classical **3** stadium **4** movie theater
5 comedy **6** actors

PRONUNCIATION

A
1 /ʊ/ **2** /uː/ **3** /ʊ/ **4** /uː/ **5** /ʊ/ **6** /uː/

B
/ʊ/ book; took
/uː/ food; school; shoe; true; two; you

C
1 I played tennis last Tuesday. /uː/
2 Stop pushing me! /ʊ/
3 Look at the rainbow! It's amazing. /ʊ/
4 I bought a new T-shirt yesterday. /uː/
5 I really like listening to rock music. /uː/
6 I can't carry this glass – it's too full! /ʊ/
7 You should eat more fruit! /uː/
8 I can't run right now, I've hurt my foot. /ʊ/

11.3 Reading; Listening

B
Suggested answer
Yes, he did. He thinks it is a good place to relax and study or work, play the piano or spend time with friends. He also likes it because it is different.

C
1 with friends **2** likes **3** free **4** food **5** can **6** One; was

LISTENING

A
b

B
concert: Stevie ✓, Ashley ✓, Molly ✗
sporting event: Stevie ✗, Ashley ✗, Molly ✓
movie night: Stevie ✓, Ashley ✓, Molly ✓

C
1 music club **2** work **3** winter **4** everybody enjoys

11.4 Functional Language; Write a personal profile

FUNCTIONAL LANGUAGE

A
1 tomorrow
2 not to go
3 relax

B
1 in the afternoon and evening
2 go swimming (at the recreation center or at the beach)
3 It's too cold.
4 going to a classical music concert
5 No, they don't.
6 listen to the jazz musicians in the park

C
1 busy **2** free **3** let's **4** How **5** don't **6** sure
7 perfect **8** meet

WRITING

A
1 takes pictures; vacation
2 alone; apartment
3 doesn't have; likes
4 enjoys

B
1 a **2** b **3** b **4** c

WRITING PRACTICE

B
Model answer
She's a writer for a fashion magazine, so she often travels to other countries to see fashion shows. It's a great job and she meets interesting people. She lives with her husband and two children in a house near the ocean. They're all soccer fans, but she doesn't like soccer at all, so when they are watching a game she takes their two dogs for a walk. She likes water sports, and when it isn't too cold, she goes swimming in the ocean. She also designs clothes and she wants to be a fashion designer.

12.1 Trips

VOCABULARY

A
1 taxi **2** airport **3** plane **4** euros **5** passports **6** bag
7 traffic **8** train **9** foot **10** luggage

B
1 ticket **2** trolleys **3** credit **4** money **5** luggage **6** bike

C
1 taxi **2** airport **3** luggage **4** traffic **5** tickets
6 credit card **7** money **8** passport

PRONUNCIATION

A
1 plane **2** class **3** station **4** blue **5** green **6** chips

GRAMMAR

A
1 a **2** a **3** b **4** b **5** b **6** a **7** a **8** a **9** b **10** a

B
1 money; credit cards **2** bottles; water
3 homework; exercises **4** food; sandwiches
5 traffic; cars **6** luggage; bags **7** music; songs
8 cash; credit cards **9** hours; time **10** food; sandwiches

12.2 A prize vacation

VOCABULARY

A
1 camera **2** camping **3** sunglasses **4** skis **5** hotel
6 tent **7** beach **8** chalet **9** skiing goggles
10 sightseeing **11** skiing **12** snorkel

B

Types of vacations: beach; camping; sightseeing; skiing
Places to stay: chalet; hotel; tent
Things you need by the ocean: camera; snorkel; sunglasses
Things you need in the mountains: camera; skiing goggles; skis; sunglasses

C

1 guidebook **2** tourists **3** on **4** around **5** from **6** in **7** with **8** with **9** stove

PRONUNCIATION

A

1 beach **2** win **3** like **4** time **5** ski **6** winner

C

1 /ɪ/ **2** /iː/ **3** /aɪ/ **4** /iː/ **5** /aɪ/ **6** /ɪ/

GRAMMAR

A

1 Where are you **going** ~~go~~ on vacation this year?
2 I'm ~~be~~ driving to Boston in the morning.
3 Judith's **meeting** ~~meet~~ Amanda at the train station.
4 **I'm going** ~~I go~~ on a sightseeing vacation next month – I'm very excited.
5 We're **leaving** ~~leave~~ at five in the morning.
6 The manager **isn't** ~~doesn't~~ working next week.
7 Are you **taking** ~~take~~ the train to Fresno?
8 **Is** ~~Does~~ your sister going on vacation with you?

B

1 N **2** F **3** N **4** F **5** F **6** N **7** N **8** F

C

1 I'm visiting
2 He's playing
3 are you doing
4 is arriving
5 They aren't/They're not working
6 are you going out

12.3 Reading; Listening

READING

B

Paul

C

Favorite type of vacation: Paul – sightseeing; Jade – camping
He/She stays in: Paul – a hotel; Jade – a tent or van
He/She likes: Paul – museums and galleries; Jade – swimming
Last year's vacation destination: Paul – Rome, Italy; Jade – California
Next year's vacation destination: Paul – Australia; Jade – Arizona
(Not used: a chalet, Cambodia, skiing)

LISTENING

A

1 B **2** S **3** B **4** W **5** B **6** B **7** W

B

1 hot place **2** by plane

C

1 isn't
2 T-shirts
3 are not
4 in the daytime and in the evening
5 a jacket
6 a snorkel
7 Claudia
8 didn't forget

12.4 Functional Language; Write a postcard

FUNCTIONAL LANGUAGE

A

a so **b** cool **c** busy **d** about **e** really **f** idea **g** think

B

1 f **2** d **3** a **4** c **5** e **6** g **7** b

WRITING

A

(in) Greece

B

a I got **here** ~~hear~~ three days ago and **I'm** ~~Im~~ going home on **S**aturday.
b One week **isn't** ~~aren't~~ long and I **can't** ~~cant~~ wait to come back again next **year** ~~yeer~~.
c **It's** ~~Its~~ hot and **sunny** ~~suny~~, so I go to the **beach** ~~beech~~ every day and swim.
d There are lots of **museums** ~~musiums~~ in **A**thens – I **went** ~~am going~~ to the Archeological Museum yesterday.

C

1 a **2** c **3** d **4** b

D

1 to the beach **2** hat and snorkel **3** Yes, she did. **4** Yes, she does.

WRITING PRACTICE

B

Model answer

Hi Jorje,

I'm taking a quick trip to Paris for three days.

The hotel is very nice. It's rainy here right now, so I got a new umbrella (I didn't bring one).

There are lots of museums and art galleries to visit. I tried to visit the Louvre yesterday, but it was very busy and there were long lines, so I went for a walk around the city.

Near the River Seine, there are lots of people selling books, so I got some interesting history books. You know I love reading about history.

I came yesterday, so tomorrow is my last day. What a shame!

See you when I get back!

Esmerelda

Notes

Notes

Notes